by the same author

THE LEOPARD

TWO STORIES AND
A MEMORY

TWO STORIES
and a MEMORY

Giuseppe di Lampedusa

Translated from the Italian by
ARCHIBALD COLQUHOUN

With an Introduction by
E. M. FORSTER

PANTHEON BOOKS

This book was first published under the title Racconti by
Feltrinelli Editore, Milan, 1961
© Giangiacomo Feltrinelli Editore, Milan, 1961
© In the English translation, Wm. Collins Sons & Co. Ltd.,
London and Pantheon Books, New York, 1962
Published by Pantheon Books, a Division of Random House, Inc.
Library of Congress Catalog Card Number: 62–14259
All rights reserved, including the right to reproduce this book
or portions thereof in any form.
Manufactured in the United States of America
by H. Wolff, New York

ACKNOWLEDGMENTS

My particular thanks are due to the Princess of Lampedusa, the author's widow, for correcting this study and adding much new material, and also for checking the translations. Other members of the author's family, particularly his adopted son, have been most helpful; and I have enjoyed many talks with his friends. One of the most fascinating afternoons I have ever spent in Sicily was with the author's cousin, the poet Barone Lucio Piccolo di Calanovella, at his remote estate behind Capo d'Orlando. My gratitude is also due to the Signorina Crescimano, of Villa Lampedusa, San Lorenzo Colle, near Palermo, for permission to reproduce the photograph of her grandfather in her possession; to Dottore Giulio Cesare Barresi of Palermo for photographing it and for permission to reproduce all the photographs of Santa Margherita Belice and Palma di Montechiaro (with the exception of the façade of Santa Margherita, for which photograph thanks are due to Alterocca of Terni); to many kind citizens of Santa Margherita Belice for showing me around; and to Dottore Andrea Vitello of Palma di Montechiaro, whose researches into the Tomasi di Lampedusa ancestry, together with much other information, are to be found in his book, *Palma di Montechiaro, Terra di "Il Gattopardo"*, published by the committee for an international study group on depressed areas organized by Danilo Dolci at Palma di Montechiaro in April, 1960.

Of writings about the Prince of Lampedusa I have found particularly perceptive and informative a series of articles on a Sicilian journey by Camilla Cederna published in *L'Espresso* during the early spring of 1962.

I alone, of course, am responsible for any opinions and interpretations here expressed.

Archibald Colquhoun

CONTENTS

ILLUSTRATIONS

INTRODUCTION

by E. M. Forster

This prefatory note is a meditation rather than an introduction. Prince Giuseppe di Lampedusa has meant so much to me that I find it impossible to present him formally. His great novel, *The Leopard* (Il Gattopardo), has certainly enlarged my life—an unusual experience for a life which is well on in its eighties. Reading and rereading it has made me realize how many ways there are of being alive, how many doors there are, close to one, which someone else's touch may open. The author was born after me and he has died before me—an unexpected sequence. He is my junior. I like to fancy that he has left me a personal legacy.

So it is a great pleasure to be connected with this volume (an excellent translation) and an austerer pleasure to announce that it is not a second masterpiece. How could it be? Leopards do not hang on every bush. It contains three items greatly differing in their character: an autobiography, a short story, and the opening chapter of an unwritten novel.

The autobiography—"Places of My Infancy"—is exquisite. It begins vaguely and unchronologically, and then, as the infant matures and observes the passage of time and the varieties of place, it coalesces, and gives an imaginative account of two houses which reappear still more imaginatively in *The Leopard*. There is the Palermo palace, figuring in both works. There is the country palace in western Sicily, Santa Margherita Belice, whose fictional counterpart is Donnafugata. Donnafugata has the lovelier name, is the more difficult to reach, has the sweeter peaches, the more dubious recesses; Santa Margherita is the unchallenged and unchangeable possession of a child. The old Prince, looking back at it, can detect falsities and stupidities that he ignored at the time, but nothing dims its general glow or the conviction that he loved everyone and everything there, and was loved.

And now for the most remarkable of the three items—
the story entitled "The Professor and the Mermaid." It
particularly interests me for the reason that, thirty years
previously, I too wrote a story about a Siren. I don't know
whether he ever read mine—he does refer to something
analogous but it is by H. G. Wells and the reference is un-
favorable. He and I certainly have points in common as
well as points of contrast. I too located my Siren in Sicily,
and in waters as glorious as I could contrive. But I kept
her under the waters—a decency he makes no effort to
imitate. Mine was cosmic, and was to stay hidden until
ritually summoned, when she would rise to the surface,
sing, destroy silence, primness, and cruelty, and save the
world. His Siren is not cosmic; she is personal, and here
she shows her superior sense. She gives her body to a number of young men, all of whom are beautiful. She explains
to them that she never kills anyone, nor does she, but no
one who has once loved her can love anyone else, so they
all end up either as suicides or as university professors.
Her name is Lighea. She is the daughter not of Mne-
mosyne, not of Urania, but of Calliope.

It is an exquisite fantasy and a sustained one: mine was
short. We shared one other point in common, which I

must mention here: we are both of us out of date on the
subject of sea. We assumed, as did the Greeks before us,
that the sea was untamable and eternal and that strength
could drown in it and beauty sport in it forever. Here we
underestimated the mightiness of Man, who now domi-
nates the sea as never before and is infecting its depths
with atomic waste. Will Man also succeed in poisoning
the solar system? It is possible: generals are already likely
to meet on the moon. What Man probably won't effect—
and here I am getting back to *The Leopard*—is the disin-
tegration of the outer galaxies. How soothing, in that
grand novel, are the astronomical passages where the hero,
who has wasted his Sicilian day, repairs to his telescope,
and looks up through the Sicilian night at the stars. What
a release to the human spirit in its struggle against human
possessiveness! There is nothing comparable to this in the
Siren story, though I catch an echo of it in "the enchantment of certain summer nights within sight of Castellamare Bay, when stars are mirrored in the sleeping sea
and the spirit of anyone lying back among the lentisks is
lost in a vortex of sky"; *"mentre il corpo, teso e all'erta,
tema l'avvicinarsi dei demoni."* The beauty of the Italian
here defies translation, so I quote the original, and the last

word in it, *demoni,* is certainly one which everyone can apprehend.

The third item, "The Blind Kittens," is less magical. It is the opening chapter of an unfinished novel which was to deal with the Newest Rich of 1900, the gross and grasping Ibba family. In *The Leopard,* a generation earlier, we encountered the New Rich in the persons of the fairly presentable Sedàra family. But the Ibbas are peasants who are unpresentable and have no wish to be presented. They stumble blindly into a world which they cannot understand but are capable of damaging. The scene closes before it has been disclosed, but one of them (we are told) will become an eminent Fascist.

That ends my meditation. Those who have read *The Leopard* will not need it. Those who have not yet read *The Leopard* may here be introduced to a great contemporary Italian novelist.

Giuseppe di Lampedusa

A NOTE
BY THE TRANSLATOR

THE UNUSUAL ORIGIN and world-wide recognition of Giuseppe di Lampedusa's novel, *Il Gattopardo,* is a literary phenomenon—referred to in Italy as *"il caso Lampedusa."*

A prince, and a Sicilian prince what's more (a species about which we catch a whiff of contempt even from Henry James), born in 1896, is found, after his death, to have produced a book which is now being acknowledged as a minor masterpiece, and also to have caused contemporary Italian literature to make a breakthrough in the international field.

On the members of the new Italian literary establishment the book has had a different impact; it has become a bogey, for the success of *Il Gattopardo,* so different in outlook from most Italian postwar literature, seems to them a sign of decadence. What most irritates them is that the Prince of Lampedusa, who belonged to a class "old and uselessly wise" and was both participant and observer in its downfall, should have projected an "Oriental fatalism" upon the misfortunes of Sicily. Not all left-wing writers have agreed with them. "One of the great books of the century, one of the great books of always" is the judgment of Aragon, the major French Communist poet. E. M. Forster has said something more about its "greatness"— "This is one of the great *lonely* books": a particularly helpful remark, since it leads to speculation about the personality of an author whose work is obviously autobiographical.

In Palermo there is no lack of information about the head of a leading family who kept to the same routine for decades; yet, the closer one thinks to approach, the more one feels the Prince of Lampedusa to have been a very private person, who successfully put up barriers around a life that was mysterious only because it looked so ordinary.

A glance at Lampedusa's heredity may throw some

light on him. His family, the Tomasi, were respectably
ancestral even for Sicily, where pedigrees count by mil-
lennia. Though not boasting descent from the Sun God
like their peers the Alliata, they could trace their line back
to Tiberius II, Emperor of Byzantium in the sixth century. His daughter married the founder of the Gens
Thomasa Leopardi, whose coat of arms with its prancing
beast, in various forms, is to be found all over southern
Europe, and which included among its septs a great poet,
Giacomo Leopardi.

By the turn of the sixteenth century, a branch of the
Tomasi were settled in Sicily. After a couple more lucra-
tive alliances, they were, by 1637, in a position to found
on their estates near Agrigento an entire new town, Palma
di Montechiaro, which incorporated the very latest theo-
ries of town planning.

Toward the end of the eighteenth century, one Don
Giuseppe Maria Tomasi-Colonna, Prince of Lampedusa,*
Duke of Palma, Baron of Montechiaro, of La Torretta

---

* Lopodosa in Latin; a little island about 125 miles to the south of
Sicily, once a bulwark against the Saracens. After the secession of Malta
to Britain in the Napoleonic Wars this island was expropriated by the
Bourbon crown as a strong point, and the last Prince of Lampedusa had
never been there.

with Falconeri, of Rafforoso, Racalzarat, and Monte Colombino, married, as his second wife, a Bavarian, Caroline von Wochenger. This lady was the mother of the next Prince of Lampedusa, Don Giulio Maria Fabrizio, distinguished mathematician and astronomer, discoverer of two asteroids to which he gave the names "Palma" and "Lampedusa," and the recipient of a prize at the Sorbonne. He married the Marchesina Maria Stella Guccia, sat in the Sicilian Chamber of Peers in 1848, and died at Florence of typhus in 1885. His body is buried above the grinning mummies in the Capuchin Friary of Palermo, near the grave of his great-grandson, Don Giuseppe Fabrizio, last Prince of Lampedusa, who used him as the original, in so far as an artist's concept has any original outside the land of poetry, for the Don Fabrizio of *Il Gattopardo*.

Lampedusa's mother, born Filangeri di Cutò, was one of five brilliant sisters brought up in France under a strong French Illuminist tradition, and perhaps, adoring his mother as he did, this influenced his attitude toward religion; certainly *Il Gattopardo* is impregnated with the transmuted spiritual yearning of a particular kind of artist who is also a non-practicing Catholic.

From his father he seems to have been estranged. Lampedusa's inheritance was relatively unencumbered, due to Don Giulio Fabrizio's leaving no will when he died so suddenly at a distant hotel. But a scandal hung over the family, which must have affected all his youth: the murder of his mother's sister, Princess Trigona di Sant' Elia, lady-in-waiting to the Queen of Italy, by her lover in a low hotel in Rome in 1911. This made his mother shut their home in Palermo and go traveling for twenty years.

As a regular officer of artillery, Lampedusa saw service on the Balkan front during the First World War. He was taken prisoner and made two attempts to escape. The second was successful; he crossed Europe in disguise and on foot.

Though he did not leave the regular service till 1925, he seems to have been hit before then by one of those mysterious postwar crises, an artist's readjustment, perhaps, or connected maybe with the sale of one of the playgrounds of his youth, the house at Santa Margherita Belice. The property there was sold up in 1921 by the last Filangeri Prince of Cutò, an uncle who ruined himself by bad management of his estates and by financing the first socialist newspaper in Sicily.

Lampedusa was always an anti-Fascist. He refused to hold public office during Fascism, and this may have been another reason for his aura of skepticism and withdrawal.

He did not marry till thirty-four, particularly late for a Sicilian.

He first met his future wife, in the mid-twenties, at the Italian Embassy in Grosvenor Square, London. Alessandra von Wolff-Stomersee, stepdaughter of the Ambassador, Marchese Tomasi della Torretta, was told to entertain the silent young relative, who arrived at the very moment that her mother and his uncle were off to Court; and, so she remembers, they talked of a mutual passion, Shakespeare, as they walked . . . to Whitechapel.

The young Baroness was of Baltic origin; her father had been a marshal at the Court of St. Petersburg.

Today, the Princess of Lampedusa is a leading Freudian analyst, a former president of the Italian Psychoanalysts' Association, one of the very few analysts in the peninsula with international qualifications, a dedicated figure and also a highly cultivated woman.

For years she and her husband spent their evenings

reading out loud, in five languages, from their favorite authors. It was the Princess who, originally to calm her husband's nostalgia, first encouraged him to write; and, as he brought home *Il Gattopardo,* in sections, from the café where he copied it out, she advised him on it.

We can picture the Prince setting off from his house in Via Butera in the morning, on his daily routine, leaving his wife to her patients. He is a quietly dressed, rather thickset figure, holding a bulky brief case, his general appearance that of a retired senior officer; which in fact he was. He threads his way among hanging laundry, screaming children, and street vendors, for Via Butera is dilapidated since the war. He goes past the building, reduced to a tenement, which once housed the Hotel Trinacria where he set Don Fabrizio's death, moves on under the vast hulk of Palazzo Butera, and out to where the baroque arms of Porta Felice once opened onto the most splendid marine drive in Europe, ruined now by debris dumped there during the last war. Whole areas of Palermo have never recovered from bombing, and one can imagine the bitter twist to Don Giuseppe's lips (it shows in most of his later photographs) as he passes Via Lampedusa and the rubble to which his old home has been reduced.

From now on, his routine—the café tables he used, the waiters who served him, even the cakes he ate—followed an invariable pattern: breakfast at the Pasticceria del Massimo in Via Maqueda; a call at Flaccovio, the imaginative bookseller and publisher whose shop is a kind of literary club, and who was the first to encourage him to publish; by midday he would be settled in his personal version of an ivory tower, the back room of the Café Mazzara under the only skyscraper in town.

The brief case opens. It contains, as well as maybe a few cakes from the last café, books, the addiction which made him as great an object of suspicion to his fellow grandees as his great-grandfather had been with his telescopes and comet finders.

The books might vary, but were all in their original language: Tolstoy, Stendhal, Flaubert and Proust, Thomas Mann, Dickens, and latterly, Virginia Woolf and E. M. Forster (it is pleasant to think of this admiration being reciprocated). Always there was a volume of Shakespeare which, according to his widow, he took with him everywhere. His knowledge of Elizabethan literature is said to have been extraordinary. This concentrated reading throughout the day at the café table (replaced only during the last years by a mysterious scribbling) was in a way creative. His cousin and intimate friend, the poet Lucio Piccolo, can remember his spending an entire summer reading the novels of Richardson, and journeying out to Capo d'Orlando every fortnight to discuss them. Some five years before Don Giuseppe died, these conversations about literature turned into lessons or lectures, for which he wrote elaborate notes; those on French literature have been preserved.

At times, when Palermo, and even more the rest of Sicily, appears to be in the grasp of some ill co-ordinated time machine gone into reverse, this little group, meeting day after day in a public place to discuss literature, might have been repeating scenes in a coffee house in eighteenth-century London, or a more ancient pattern of master and pupil in the Agora in Athens.

We would expect Lampedusa to have been a much traveled man. To Sicilians, the capital is still Paris, with London for clothes and accouterments; and certainly a love of things French is reflected in nearly everything Don Giuseppe wrote.

Anglophilia about clothes has of course been general in Europe for a couple of centuries, but it was surely taken to extremes by the Sicilian whose valet ran into his master's bedroom on their first morning in London to report that he was "the only man dressed like an English-man in London."

When Lampedusa first came to London, his friends were "people round the Embassy." Either he was too shy, or too proud, or merely too lazy to try to meet anyone on a level with his own literary standards. During later visits, most of his time was spent at bookstalls in the Charing Cross Road. But he also traveled in the English country-side, and Piccolo tells us that after one such trip he ex-claimed, "The castles! The parks! The deer!" He had been staying at Powis Castle in Wales.

In Italy, Lampedusa traveled little after the early twen-ties, when he had been around Europe with his mother. But one visit to the mainland had important results. In the summer of 1954, as companion to his cousin Lucio Piccolo, who was to receive a prize for his poems, he attended a literary congress at San Pellegrino Terme. The assembled Italian *literati* thought they were granting an accolade to an unknown adolescent, but instead of *"l'éphèbe en blue jeans qu'on attendait"* (according to an account of the episode in Paris *Match*) a grave Sicilian gentleman in clothes of antique cut advanced to the rostrum. With him, to complete the general bewilderment, was a man of military aspect, introduced as the Prince of Lampedusa, accompanied by a sun-blackened retainer, who followed the pair everywhere. Giorgio Bassani, who was to be the first to recognize the merit of the anonymous manuscript of *Il Gattopardo* and is largely responsible for its present form, remembers Piccolo's cousin bowing gravely and remaining silent.

It was a year after this congress that Lampedusa finally got down to writing the novel he had talked about off and on for twenty-five years.

Having sketched in Lampedusa's background, we might glance at the places which affected him most deeply and are reflected in his writings: the family palace in Palermo, the Cutò villa at Santa Margherita Belice, and the Tomasi estates at Palma di Montechiaro. All these, transformed by his artist's eye, contributed to the imaginary palace and town of Donnafugata in *Il Gattopardo*.

From Palazzo Lampedusa, deep in old Palermo behind

the Dominican monastery and near the Oratory of Santa
Zita, came the sense of a great house rising from slums, its
vastness, the enfilade of drawing rooms dappled with sunbeams on red and gold, the warren of passages. One custom from that house was transplanted to a later home,
where it can be heard today: a system of handbells rung
by a porter in the entrance courtyard to warn servants upstairs of who had entered; now a bent crone rings a hand-
bell twice for a man, once for a woman, and one and a
half times for a priest.

In 1943, during the so-called "carpet" bombing of
Palermo that preceded the American landing, "a bomb
manufactured in Pittsburgh, Pennsylvania," totally destroyed the old Palazzo Lampedusa. Only a length of
wall and a mass of rubble now remain. Don Giuseppe was
a refugee in the hills at the time; he had escaped, the story
goes, on a bicycle, with the family Bellini and his wife's
furs on his handlebars. On his return, he found that even
old photographs, like those of the Greek statues mentioned in the last bitter lines of "The Professor and the
Mermaid," had been used as torches by the looters. The
total loss of his home (the Sicilian attachment to old

homes and possessions belongs to a world before death duties or the National Trust) weighed more and more heavily on Don Giuseppe's spirits. Even the purchase, from the Knights of Malta, of the house by the sea where the original Gattopardo had spent his summers did not assuage his nostalgia.

Yet in the end he drew an enrichment from his loss. Persuaded by his wife that to write a description of his lost home would be the best therapy, he sat down ten years later and produced the beautiful fragment "Places of My Infancy." This was never intended for publication and never revised. But, as memories linked, the suppressed artist took over and the descriptions of the palace at Palermo and of the Cutò house at Santa Margherita Belice became the first inspiration for the imaginary Donnafugata of the novel.

Luckily the house at Santa Margherita is still in good enough repair to show how close this country palace is to the one in the novel.

Its scale is smaller, and the description of it as a "little Vatican" may be due to one of those enlargement tricks of childhood memory, but the present owners have counted

110 rooms. There are still to be seen three courtyards, the main façade (dated 1751), and the row of library-ballroom windows looking over the square. This square is not quite as Don Fabrizio saw it when he looked out at Tancredi going courting, for the ground level has been raised, and this plays havoc with the front view of the house; but the air of poetic gaiety which once enveloped the palace can still be sensed.

Even the magic of the garden is not entirely lost, though the fountain of Amphitrite is sadly despoiled and there are no monkeys now in the rusticated cage that ends the vista. In what was called, after the visit of the Crown Prince of Naples, the Leopard drawing room, still hung, (until this spring,) paintings of the Filangeri family at breakfast two hundred years ago.

Certainly from this house came the concept of a Sicilian *vie de château,* a custom quite unknown in Sicily in 1860 and little appreciated even now. It must have been an importation from France by the Filangeri family, as was the private theater at Santa Margherita, with a coquettish flight of rococo steps on one side of the façade. Alas, within only the last five years the remains of the velvet Louis Seize boxes and stalls have been stripped away and

1. *The author in the grounds of Castle Stomersee in Lettonia, 1936. (The spaniel was called Crab, after Crab in* Two Gentlemen of Verona.)

2. *The author, 1946.*

3. *The author's widow on the terrace of the present Palazzo Lampedusa, which figured in* The Leopard *as a summer palace by the sea.*

4. *Left to right: Gioacchino Lanza, adopted son of the author and **now** Duke of Palma, the model of Tancredi; Barone Lucio Piccolo, the author's cousin; the author.*

5. One of the last photographs taken of the author, 1955.

6. *A portrait of Don Giulio Maria Fabrizio Tomasi, Prince of Lampedusa, the original of the Leopard, about 1860.*

7. *A photograph of Don Fabrizio in late middle age.*

the husk of the place, its form still clearly discernible, is now a cinema; backstage is the warren of passages described in "Places of My Infancy."

That essay mentions a story attached to this house which may possibly explain the origin of the name *Donnafugata*—though the Arabic word means, "enclosed fountain," in Italian its literal meaning could be "woman fled." In the winter of 1813-14 the Cutò house at Santa Margherita was part refuge, part prison, to Queen Maria Carolina of Naples before she set off on her last journey to death in Vienna. A memento of that distant British occupation, when Bentinck, the British High Commissioner, posted a garrison to the town as jailers, is still to be seen in the public gardens just outside the town. There, described as only a kiosk in the memoir, is a small colonnaded temple in Adam style, still known locally by the mysterious syllables *"Il coffee-house."* From it, a statue gazes out over the vast vale of central Sicily, with its scattered villages and towns and on its slopes the patches of yellow wheat, interspersed with burnt stubble, which already as a boy reminded Don Giuseppe of a crouching wild beast.

Locals can still remember him riding out through these

public gardens, a sturdy young figure, followed by a cockaded groom. Nor have the autumn arrivals of the family been forgotten. In the memory of one returned immigrant, in the year he came back from America, 1913, the family that alighted at the town gates from a gilded coach, to the strains of "Noi siamo zingarelle," were all dressed in white. Perhaps the scene was transmuted by memory, for the coaches were certainly traveling landaus and the passengers may have been white with dust.

In "Places of My Infancy" there is no more than a mention of the third house, at Palma di Montechiaro, and it is only to say that the family never went there.

No place could have been less suitable for children than the dank palace of the seventeenth-century Saint-Duke, Don Giulio Tomasi, who "had scourged himself alone, in the sight of God and his estates, when it must have seemed to him that the drops of his own blood were about to rain down on the land and redeem it." Suffering is in the air at Palma di Montechiaro.

Visitors to Palma (which is crossed, improbably, by the main coast road around the island) are advised to look out for a timeless little square, dust-swept and sunscorched, on the side of which rise the ramps and barricades of the Convent of the Holy Ghost. According to local accounts, Don Giuseppe visited these dilapidated feudal remains twice or more after the war. These were undoubtedly the inspiration for the town of Donnafugata "apparently despairing" in its misery and disease. There too, as in the novel, is the church with its great flight of steps and squat columns.

Nowadays, local memories of the Tomasi family, apart from an occasional Leopard Rampant crumbling above a doorway, are mainly confined to the Saint-Duke's two children, both at the moment (and for the last two hundred years or more) under official process for canonization. One, the Blessed Cardinal Giuseppe Maria Tomasi, was the initiator of liturgical reforms that have been promulgated throughout the Church in the last few years. The other, the Venerable Suor Maria Crocifissa, was a visionary in the Spanish style of the day (she figures in *Il Gattopardo* as the Blessed Corbèra); her votive cards are in prayerbooks all over the province, where she is deeply venerated, and she certainly means more locally than any other member of the family before or since.

In this convent, which she founded, the stone said to have been flung at her by the Devil can still be seen, and nearby a letter he wrote her on that occasion. At a rotating wheel in the convent parlor can be acquired those almond cakes so enjoyed by Don Fabrizio and his family on their visits, and still made by the nuns "on an ancient recipe." But the convent is strictly enclosed and the male visitor is unlikely to be allowed through a certain massive door into the freshness of the cloister where the murmur of assembled nuns greeted the Salina family in the book; the only men permitted entry are the King and the head of the Foundress's family "together with two gentlemen of his suite if the Abbess so permits."

This privilege, those cakes, the remote tinkle of a silver bell, a sprig of jasmine presented on a salver to sniff before departure, all tugged at the heart of Giuseppe di Lampedusa, last male of the Foundress's family, when he called there on a drive one winter afternoon in 1955. According to his adopted son, who accompanied him on this visit as "gentleman of the suite," the episode was most important in the genesis of *Il Gattopardo*.

At this stage, what looks like a diagram of sources can be drawn up. Members of the Lampedusa family of a hundred years ago are mentioned in the novel by their real

names, including Don Fabrizio's daughters; and the young
priest, who was really chaplain to the Lampedusa sisters
as in the final chapter of *Il Gattopardo,* can still be found,
now a Monsignor, in Palermo.

What emerges from such investigations is that details
taken straight from life set and enhance the different treatment of major characters and themes, giving the reader
a sense of being "right there" and helping to provide a
kind of stereoscopic vision. The character of Don Fabrizio
is neither historical symbol, family memoir, self-portrait,
nor wish fulfillment, and yet something of all four. Tancredi is another instance of a multiple source; he is drawn
from two possible historical figures, and maybe the person
of Don Giuseppe's adopted son, now (thanks to the permission of ex-King Umberto) Duke of Palma. So, too, the
arrival of the Garibaldini in 1860 seems to have merged
with memories of the Allies' invasion of Sicily in 1943. A
cousin, Prince Niscèmi, remembers a conversation about a
projected last chapter to be based on the actual arrival of
the American troops. This might have been fascinatingly
ironic ("If we want things to stay as they are, things will
have to change") for the liberation of Palermo was rich
with anticlimax, the terror of the inhabitants soon turning

into Te Deums and kinship hunts. It never got written—
unless the shelves of the Lampedusa library produce any
more notebooks covered with Don Giuseppe's crabbed
handwriting. The carrying power of *Il Gattopardo,* however, is not due to any correspondence of incident and
character with reality, and certainly to no political im-
plications, but to its poetry about the human condition.

Is the novel the peaks, in a more or less continuous
range, of a vast submerged book that was never com-
pleted? Each episode stands out almost by itself; yet it is
astonishing how the whole novel holds together, con-
sidering that the great ball scene (the last to be written)
was found separately in Rome; that the chapter about
Father Pirrone at San Cono was probably intended as a
separate story and grafted onto the book, and that there
exist six pages of a chapter which give a glimpse of Don
Fabrizio's sudden passion for Angelica (he learns that she
is going to a rendezvous with a lover and substitutes himself).

It is odd that the concept of a suitable death, explored
in that superb chapter "Death of a Prince," taken partly
from his grandfather's at a hotel in Florence, should have

become partial reality when Don Giuseppe himself died from cancer, in a little room in Rome, in 1957.

A moment before his death (by a stroke of irony he might have appreciated) he was chatting quietly with the doctor about a baroque courtyard in Palermo to which an American bomb had brought sudden destruction.

"Art has two constant and unending preoccupations; it is always meditating upon death and it is thereby creating life." That description of an imaginary death finally removed the stoppage to creative writing that had been with Giuseppe di Lampedusa for so long. Once he started, he went on creating, and the pages which follow—together with some papers on French literature—are the fruit of this late flowering.

A.C.

Places of My Infancy

A MEMORY

[*Summer, 1955*]

I

With everyone, I think, memories of early childhood consist of a series of visual impressions, many very clear but lacking any sense of chronology. To write a "chronicle" of one's own childhood is, it seems, impossible; however honest one might set out to be one would eventually give a false impression, often with glaring anachronisms. I shall therefore adopt the method of grouping my subjects together, so trying to give an overall impression in space rather than by sequence of time. I will touch on the background of my childhood and on the people forming part of it; also on my feelings, though

I will not try to follow the development of these from their origins.

I can promise to say nothing that is untrue, but do not think I shall want to say all; and I reserve the right to lie by omission. Unless I change my mind.

One of the oldest memories I can set exactly in time, as it is connected with a fact verifiable historically, goes back to the thirtieth of July, 1900, and so to the time when I was a few days over three and a half years old.

I was with my mother in her dressing room, with her maid (probably Teresa from Turin). It was a rectangular room whose windows gave onto a pair of balconies projecting from the shorter sides, one of them looking over a narrow garden that separated our house from the Oratory of Santa Zita, the other over a small inner courtyard. The dressing table, kidney-shaped, with a pink material showing through its glass top and legs enwrapped in a kind of white lace petticoat, was set facing the balcony overlooking the little garden; on it, as well as brushes and toilet implements, stood a big mirror in a frame also made of mirror, decorated with stars and other glass ornaments which were a delight to me.

44

It was about eleven in the morning, I think, and I can see the great light of summer coming through the open French windows, whose shutters were closed.

My mother was combing her hair with the help of her maid, and I do not know what I could have been doing, sitting on the floor in the middle of the room. I don't know if my nurse, Elvira the Sienese, was with us too, but I think not.

Suddenly we hear hurried steps coming up the little inner staircase communicating with my father's apartments on the lower or *mezzanine* floor directly beneath; he enters without knocking, and utters some phrase in an excited tone. I remember his manner very well, but not his words nor their sense.

I can "see" still, though, the effect they produced; my mother dropped the long-handled silver brush she was holding, Teresa said, *"Bon Signour!"* and the whole room was in consternation.

My father had come to announce the assassination of King Umberto at Monza the evening before, the twenty-ninth of July, 1900. I repeat that I "see" every streak of light and shade from the balcony, "hear" my father's ex-

45

cited voice, the sound of the brush falling on the glass
table top, good Teresa's exclamation in Piedmontese, that
I "feel" the sense of dismay which overwhelmed us; but
all this remains personal, detached from the news of the
King's death. The historic meaning, as it were, was told
me later, and may serve to explain the persistence of the
scene in my memory.

Another of the memories which I can clearly distinguish
is that of the Messina earthquake (twenty-eighth of De-
cember, 1908). The shock was certainly felt at Palermo, but
I have no memory of that; I suppose it did not interrupt
my sleep. But I can see distinctly the hands of my grandfather's big English pendulum clock, which was then in
the great entrance hall, stopped at the fatal hour of twenty
past five; and I can still hear one of my uncles (I think
Ferdinando, who was mad about watchmaking) explain
to me that it had been stopped by an earthquake during
the night. Then I remember that same evening, about
half past seven, being in my grandparents' dining room
(I used often to be present at their dinner, as it took place
before mine) when an uncle, probably the same Ferdinando, came in with an evening paper which announced

"serious damage and numerous victims at Messina from this morning's earthquake."

This memory is much less lively visually than the first, though much more exact on the other hand from the point of view of a "thing that happened."

Some days later there arrived from Messina a cousin of mine who had lost his father and mother in the earthquake. He went to stay with my cousins the Piccolos, and I remember my going there to pay him a visit on a bleak rainy winter's day. I can still see my mother's grief when, quite a few days later, came news of her sister Lina's and her brother-in-law's bodies having been found. I can see my mother sobbing in a big armchair in which no one ever sat in the green drawing room, wearing a short cape of moiré astrakhan. Big army wagons were going around the streets collecting clothes and blankets for refugees; one passed along Via Lampedusa, and I handed woolen blankets from one of our balconies over to a soldier standing up on a cart and almost level with the balcony. This soldier was an artilleryman, with orange braid on his blue cap; I can still see his rubicund face and hear his "Thank you, my boy," in a mainland accent. I have a memory, too, of a rumor going around

47

that the refugees, who were lodged everywhere, even in boxes at theaters, were behaving "most indecently" among themselves, and of my father saying with a smile, "They feel an urge to replace the dead," an allusion which I understood perfectly.

There is another day also clearly stamped on my memory; I cannot get the date exactly, but it was certainly a long time before the Messina earthquake and shortly after King Umberto's death, I think. We were guests of the Florios at their villa of Favignana, at the height of summer. I remember Elvira, my nurse, coming to wake me up earlier than usual, about seven, hurriedly passing a sponge full of cold water over my face and then dressing me with great care. I was dragged downstairs, went out through a little side door to the garden, then was made to climb up onto the villa's main entrance veranda, overlooking the sea and reached by a flight of some six or seven steps. I remember the blinding sun of that early morning of July or August. On the veranda, which was protected from the sun by great curtains of orange cloth swelling and flapping like sails in the sea breeze (I can still hear the sound), my mother, Signora Florio (the "divinely lovely" Franca), and others were sitting on cane chairs. In the center of the group sat a very old, very bent lady with an aquiline nose, enwrapped in widow's weeds which were waving wildly about in the wind. I was brought before her; she said a few words which I did not understand and, bending down even farther, gave me a kiss on the forehead. (I must have been very small indeed if a lady sitting down had to bend down even farther to kiss me.) After this I was taken back to my room, stripped of my finery, re-dressed in more modest garments, and led onto the beach to join the Florio children and others; with them I bathed and we stayed for a long time under a broiling sun playing our favorite game, which was searching in the sand for the pieces of deep red coral occasionally to be found there.

That afternoon it was revealed that the old lady had been Eugénie, ex-Empress of the French, whose yacht was anchored off Favignana; she had dined with the Florios the night before (without, of course, my knowing anything about it) and had paid a farewell visit at seven next morning (thus with imperial nonchalance inflicting real torture on my mother and on Signora Florio) in the course of which she asked to meet the younger members of the household.

During these last few days (mid-June, 1955) I have been rereading Stendhal's *Henri Brulard*. I had not read it since long ago in 1922, when I must have still been obsessed by "explicit beauty" and "subjective interest," for I remember not liking the book.

Now I cannot but agree with anyone who judges it to be Stendhal's masterpiece; it has an immediacy of feeling, an obvious sincerity, a remarkable attempt to sweep away accumulated memories and reach the essence. And what lucidity of style! What a mass of reflections, the more precious for being common to all men!

I should like to try and do the same. Indeed, it seems obligatory. When one reaches the decline of life it is imperative to try and gather together as many as possible of the sensations which have passed through our particular organism. Few can succeed in thus creating a masterpiece (Rousseau, Stendhal, Proust) but all should find it possible to preserve in some such way things which without this slight effort would be lost forever. To keep a diary, or write down one's own memories at a certain age, should be a duty "state-imposed"; material thus accumulated would have inestimable value after three or four generations; many of the psychological and historical problems that assail humanity would be resolved. There are no memoirs, even those written by insignificant people, which do not include social and graphic details of first-rate importance.

The extraordinary interest that Defoe's novels aroused is due to the fact that they are near-diaries, brilliant though apocryphal. What, one wonders, would genuine ones have been like? Imagine, say, the diary of a Parisian procuress of the *Régence,* or the memories of Byron's valet during the Venetian period!

But I find I cannot follow Stendhal in "quality" of memory. He interprets his childhood as a time when he was bullied and tyrannized. For me childhood is a lost paradise. Everyone was good to me—I was king of the home—even people later hostile to me were then *aux petits soins.*

So the reader (who won't exist) must expect to be led meandering through a lost Earthly Paradise. If it bores him, I don't mind.

51

CASA LAMPEDUSA

First of all, our home. I loved it with utter abandon, and still love it now when for the last twelve years it
has been no more than a memory. Until a few months before its destruction I used to sleep in the room where I was
born, five yards away from the spot where my mother's
bed had stood when she bore me. And in that house, in
that very room maybe, I was glad to feel a certainty of
dying. All my other homes (very few, actually, apart
from hotels) have merely been roofs which have served
to shelter me from rain and sun, not homes in the traditional and venerable sense of that word.

So it will be very painful for me to evoke my dead Beloved as she was until 1929 in her integrity and beauty, and as she continued after all to be until the fifth of April, 1943, the day on which bombs brought from beyond the Atlantic searched her out and destroyed her.

The first impression that remains with me is that of her vastness, and this impression is due not to the magnifying process which affects all that surrounds one's childhood, but to actual reality. When I saw the area covered by the unsightly ruins I found it was about 1,600 square yards in extent. With only ourselves living in one wing, my paternal grandparents in another, my bachelor uncles on the second floor, for twenty years it was all at my disposal, with its three courtyards, four terraces, garden, huge staircases, halls, corridors, stables, little rooms on the *mezzanine* for servants and offices—a real kingdom for a boy alone, a kingdom either empty or sparsely populated by figures unanimously well-affected.

At no point on earth, I'm sure, has sky ever stretched more violently blue than it did above our enclosed terrace, never has sun thrown gentler rays than those penetrating the half-closed shutters of the "green drawing room," never have damp-marks on a courtyard's outer walls presented shapes more stimulating to the imagination than those at my home.

I loved everything about it: the irregularity of its walls, the number of its reception rooms, the stucco of its ceilings, the smell from my grandparents' kitchen, the scent of violets in my mother's dressing room, the stuffiness of its stables, the good feel of polished leather in its saddle rooms, the mystery of some unfinished apartments on the top floor, the huge coach house in which our carriages were kept; a whole world full of sweet mysteries, of surprises ever renewed and ever fresh.

I was its absolute master and would run continually through its vast expanses, climbing the great staircase from the courtyard to the loggia on the roof, from which could be seen the sea and Mount Pellegrino and the whole city as far as Porta Nuova and Monreale. And knowing how by devious routes and turns to avoid inhabited rooms, I would feel alone and dictatorial, followed often only by my friend Tom running excitedly at my heels, with his red tongue dangling from his dear black muzzle.

The house (and I prefer to call it a house rather than a palace, a word which has been debased in Italy, applied as it is nowadays even to blocks fifteen stories high) was

tucked away in one of the most secluded streets of old
Palermo, in Via Lampedusa, at number 17, the uneven
number's evil omen then serving only to add a pleasantly
sinister flavor to the joy that it dispensed. (When later
the stables were transformed into storerooms we asked
for the number to be changed, and it became 23 when
the end was near; so number 17 had after all been lucky.)

The street was secluded but not so very narrow, and
well paved; nor was it dirty as might be thought, for opposite our entrance and along the whole length of the
building extended the old Pietrapersia palace which had
no shops or dwellings on the ground floor, its austere,
clean front in local white and yellow punctuated by numerous windows protected by enormous grilles, conferring
on it the dignified and gloomy air of an old convent or
state prison. The bomb explosions later flung many of
those heavy grilles into our rooms opposite, with what
happy effect on the old stucco work and Murano chandeliers can be imagined.

But if Via Lampedusa was decent enough, for the whole
length of our house at least, the streets into it were not;
Via Bara all'Olivella, leading into Piazza Massimo, was
crawling with poverty and squalor, and depressing to pass

along. It became slightly better when Via Roma was cut through, but there always remained a good stretch of filth and horrors to traverse.

The façade of the house had no particular architectural merit: it was white with wide borders around the windows of sulphur yellow, in purest Sicilian style of the seventeenth and eighteenth centuries, in fact. It extended along Via Lampedusa for some seventy yards or so, and had nine big balconies on the front. There were two gateways almost at the corners of the building, of enormous width as they used to be made in olden days to allow carriages to turn in from narrow streets. And in fact there was easy room even for the four-horsed teams which my father drove with mastery to race meetings at La Favorita.

Just inside the main gate which we always used rose the stairs, faced by a colonnade of fine gray Billiemi stone supporting the overhanging *tocchetto* or gallery. Beyond this gate in fact lay the main courtyard, cobbled and divided into sections by rows of flagstones. At the far end three great arches, also supported on columns of Billiemi stone, bore a terrace which linked the two wings of the house at that point.

The main staircase was a very fine one, all in gray

Billiemi, with two flights of fifteen steps or so each, set between yellowish walls. Where the second flight began there was a wide oblong landing with two mahogany doors, one facing each flight of stairs, with bulging little gilt balconies above.

Just past the entrance to the stairs, but on the exterior, in the courtyard, hung the red cord of a bell which the porter was supposed to ring in order to warn servants of their mistress's return, or the approach of visitors. The number of rings, which the porters gave with great skill, obtaining, I don't know how, sharp separate strokes without any tiresome tinkling, was rigorously laid down by protocol: four strokes for my grandmother the Princess and two for her visitors, three for my mother the Duchess and one for her visitors. But misunderstandings would occur, so that when at times my mother, my grandmother, and some friend picked up on the way entered in the same carriage a real concert would ring out of four plus three plus two strokes which were never ending. The masters, my grandfather and father, left and returned without any bell ringing for them at all.

The second flight of stairs came out onto the wide luminous *tocchetto,* which was a gallery with the spaces between its columns filled in, for reasons of comfort, by big windows with opaque lozenge-shaped panes. This contained a few sparse pieces of furniture, some big portraits of ancestors, and a large table to the left on which were put letters on arrival (it was then I read a postcard addressed to my uncle from Paris, on which some French tart had written: *"Dis à ton ami qu'il est un mufle"*). Opening out of this was an immense hall flagged in white and gray marble, with three balconies over Via Lampedusa. To my parents' great regret, its decoration was entirely modern, as in 1848 a bomb had destroyed the fine painted ceiling and irreparably damaged the wall frescoes. For a long time, it seems, a fig tree flourished in there. The hall was done up when my grandfather married, that is in 1866 or '67, all in white stucco with a *lambris* of gray marble. It was in this great hall that the footmen waited, lounging in their chairs and ready to hurry out into the *tocchetto* at the sound of that bell below.

A door with green hangings gave onto the antechamber, with six portraits of ancestors hung above its balcony entrance and its two doors, walls of gray silk, and other pictures. And from there the eye fell on a perspective of drawing rooms extending one after the other the length of the façade. Here for me began the magic of light, which in a city with so intense a sun as Palermo is concentrated or variegated according to the weather even in narrow streets. This light was sometimes diluted by the silk curtains hanging before balconies, or heightened by beating on some gilt frame or yellow damask chair which reflected it back; sometimes, particularly in summer, these rooms were dark, yet through the closed blinds filtered a sense of the luminous power that was outside; or sometimes at certain hours a single ray would penetrate straight and clear as that of Sinai, populated with myriads of dust particles and going on to vivify the colors of carpets, uniformly ruby red throughout all the drawing rooms: a real sorcery of illumination and color which entranced my mind forever. Sometimes I rediscover this luminous quality in some old palace or church, and it would wrench at my heart were I not ready to brush it aside with some "wicked joke." *

After the antechamber came the *"lambris* room," so called because its walls were covered halfway up by paneling of inlaid walnut; next the so-called " supper room,"

* In English in the Italian text.

its walls covered with dark flowered orange-colored silk, part of which still survives as wall coverings in my wife's room now. And to the left was the great ballroom with its painted floor and its ceiling on which delicious gold and yellow twirls framed mythological scenes where with rude energy and amid swirling robes crowded all the deities of Olympus.

After that came my mother's boudoir, very lovely, its ceiling scattered with flowers and branches of old colored stucco, in a design gentle and corporeal as a music by Mozart.

III

THE JOURNEY

But the house in Palermo had dependencies in
the country which multiplied its charms. These were four:
Santa Margherita Belice, a villa at Baghería, a palace at
Torretta, and a country house at Raitano. Then there was
also the old home of the family at Palma and the castle of
Montechiaro, but to those we never went.

The favorite was Santa Margherita, in which we would
spend long months even of winter. It was one of the loveliest country houses I have ever seen. Built in 1680, it had
been completely restored about 1810 by Prince Niccolò
Filangeri di Cutò, my mother's great-grandfather, on the

occasion of a long sojourn there made by Ferdinand IV and Maria Carolina, forced to reside in Sicily during the years Murat was reigning in Naples. Afterward, though, it had not been abandoned as were all other houses in Sicily, but constantly looked after, restored, and enriched until the days of my grandmother Cutò, who, having lived in Paris until the age of twenty, had not inherited the Sicilian aversion for country life; she was in residence there almost continuously and brought it "up to date" (for the Second Empire, of course, which was not very different from the general standard of comfort throughout Europe until 1914).

The charm of adventure, of the not wholly comprehensible, which is so much part of my memories of Santa Margherita, began with the journey there. This was an enterprise full of discomforts and delights. At that time there were no automobiles; around 1905 the only one that circulated around Palermo was old Signora Giovanna Florio's "*électrique.*" A train left the Lolli railroad station at ten past five in the morning. So we had to get up at half past three. Awakening at that hour was always nasty and made all the more miserable for me by the fact that it was the time at which I was given castor oil when I had stomach-ache. Servants and cooks had already left the day before. We were bundled into two closed landaus: in the first my father and mother, the governess, and myself; in the second Teresa, or Concettina maybe, my mother's maid, our accountant coming to spend holidays with his family, and Paolo, my father's valet. Another vehicle followed, I think, with luggage and hampers for luncheon.

It was usually about the end of June and dawn would be just spreading over the deserted streets. Across Piazza Politeama and Via Dante (then called Via Esposizione) we reached the Lolli railroad station, where we packed into the train for Trapani. Trains then had no corridors, and so no lavatories; and when I was very small there was brought along for my use a chamber pot in ghastly brown china bought on purpose and flung out of the window before reaching our destination. The ticket collector would do his rounds by grappling along the exterior of the exterior of the coaches, and all at once we would see his braided cap and black-gloved hand rising outside.

For hours then we crossed the lovely, desperately sad landscape of western Sicily; it must have been, I think, just exactly the same as the Thousand had found it on landing—Carini, Cinisi, Zucco, Partinico; then the line went along the sea, the rails seeming laid on the sand itself; the sun, already hot, was broiling us in our iron box, and there were no refreshments to be expected at any station. The train next cut inland, among stony hills and fields of mown wheat, yellow as the manes of lions. Eventually at eleven we reached Castelvetrano, then far from being the spry, thrusting little town it is now; it was a dreary place, with open drains and pigs walking in the main street, and flies by the billion. At the station, which had already been roasting under the sun for six hours, were waiting our carriages, two landaus to which had been fixed yellow curtains.

At half past eleven we set off again; for an hour, as far as Partanna, the road was level and easy, across fine, culti-vated country; we began to recognize places we knew, a pair of majolica Negroes' heads on the entrance pillars of a villa, an iron cross commemorating a murder; as we drew closer beneath Partanna, however, the scene changed: three *carabinieri* appeared, a sergeant and two troopers on horseback, the napes of their necks protected by patches of white cloth like horsemen in Fattori's pic-tures, who were to accompany us as far as Santa Marghe-rita. The road became mountainous: around us unrolled

64

8. *The family gallery in the church at Santa Margherita Belice, described in "Places of My Infancy."*

9. *The Filangeri di Cutò family at breakfast, a mural in the dining room at Santa Margherita.*

10. *Santa Margherita Belice: the façade of the palace and church. The level of the square has risen with the years to distort the proportions of the buildings.*

11. The garden at Santa Margherita Belice. "In the furnace of summer it was a paradise of parched scents."

12. Part of a remaining fountain in the garden at Santa Margherita. "The water came spurting in minute jets, spattering and pattering on the greenish surface."

the immeasurable scenery of feudal Sicily, desolate, breath-
less, oppressed by a leaden sun. We looked about for a tree
under whose shade to lunch; but there were only scraggy
olives which gave no shelter from the sun. Eventually an
abandoned peasant's hut was found, half in ruins, but with
its windows carefully closed. In its shade we alighted and
ate, succulent things mostly. Slightly apart, the *carabinieri,*
who had bread, meat, cakes, and bottles sent over to them,
made a gay luncheon of their own, untroubled by the
burning sun. At the end of the meal the sergeant came up
holding a brimming glass: "I thank Your Excellencies on
behalf of myself and my men!" And he took a gulp of
wine which must have had a temperature of 104 degrees.

But one of the soldiers had remained on foot, watchfully
wandering around the hut.

Back we got into the carriages. It was now two o'clock
—the truly ghastly hour of the Sicilian countryside in summer. We were moving at walking pace, for the slope down
toward the Belice River was now starting. All were silent,
and the only sound to be heard through the stamp of hoofs
was the voice of a *carabiniere* humming "La Spagnola sa
amar cosi." * Dust rose. Then we were across the Belice,

* "That's how a Spanish woman loves."

a real and proper river for Sicily—it even had water in its bed—and began the interminable ascent at walking pace; bend succeeded bend eternally in the chalky landscape.

It seemed never ending, and yet it did end. At the top of the slope the horses stopped, steaming with sweat; the *carabinieri* dismounted, we too alighted to stretch our legs. Then off we set again at a trot.

My mother was now beginning to warn me.

"Watch out now, soon on the left we'll see La Venaría." In fact we were now passing over a bridge and there on the left at last glimpsed a little verdure, some bamboo, even a patch or so of orange grove. This was Le Dàgari, the first Cutò property on our road. And behind Le Dàgari was a steep hill, traversed to the top by a wide alley of cypresses leading to La Venaría, a hunting lodge of ours.

We were not far off now. My mother, on tenterhooks because of her love for Santa Margherita, could no longer sit still and kept on craning out of one window or another. "We're nearly at Montevago." "We're home!" Across Montevago we drove, first nucleus of life seen after four hours on the road. What a nucleus though! Wide deserted streets, houses weighed down equally by poverty and by implacable sun, not a living soul, only a few pigs and some cats' carcasses.

But once past Montevago everything improved. The road was straight and level, the countryside smiling. "There's X's villa! There's the Madonna of Graces and its cypresses!" and she even hailed the cemetery with delight. Then the Madonna of Trapani. "We've arrived—there's the bridge!"

It was five in the afternoon. We had been traveling for twelve hours. On the bridge was lined up the municipal band, which broke into a lively polka. Exhausted as we were, with eyebrows white with dust and throats parched, we forced ourselves to smile and thank. A short drive through the streets and we came out into the piazza, saw the graceful lines of our home, and entered its gateway; first courtyard, passageway, second courtyard. We had arrived. At the bottom of the external staircase stood a little group of retainers, headed by our excellent agent, tiny beneath his white beard and flanked by his powerful wife. "Welcome!" "We're so pleased to have arrived!"

Up in one of the drawing rooms the agent had prepared crushed ice and lemon drinks, badly made but a blessing all the same. I was dragged off by Anna to my room and plunged, reluctant, into a tepid bath which the agent, peerless man, had thought of having ready, while my wretched parents faced the hordes of acquaintances already beginning to arrive.

IV

THE HOUSE

Set in the middle of the town, right on the leafy square, it spread over a vast expanse and contained about a hundred rooms, large and small. It gave the impression of an enclosed and self-sufficient entity, of a kind of Vatican as it were, that included state rooms, living rooms, quarters for thirty guests, servants' rooms, three enormous courtyards, stables and coach houses, a private theater and church, a large and very lovely garden, and a great orchard.

And what rooms they were! Prince Niccolò had had the good taste, almost unique for his time, not to ruin the eighteenth-century salons. In the state apartments every door was framed on both sides by fantastic friezes in gray, black, or red marble, whose harmonious asymmetry sounded a gay fanfare at everyone passing from one room to another. From the second courtyard a wide balustraded staircase of green marble, in a single flight, led up to a terrace on which opened the great entrance doors, surmounted by the belled cross of the Cutò arms.

These led into a broad entrance hall, its walls entirely covered with two ranks, one above the other, of pictures representing the Filangeri family from 1080 until my grandmother's father: all life-size standing figures in a great variety of costume, from a Crusader's to a gentleman's-in-waiting to Ferdinand II, pictures which in spite of their mediocre workmanship filled the immense room with lively familiar presences. Beneath each, in white letters on a black background, were written their names and titles, and the chief events of their lives. "Riccardo, defended Antioch against the Infidels"; "Raimondo, wounded in the defense of Acre"; another Riccardo, "chief instigator of the Sicilian Revolt" (that is, of the Sicilian Vespers); Niccolò I, "led two Hussar regiments against the Gallic hordes in 1796."

In all four corners were bronze statues of warriors in armor, a concession to the taste of the period, each holding on high a simple oil lamp. On the ceiling Jupiter, wrapped in a lilac cloud, blessed the embarkation of Roger as he prepared to sail from his native Normandy for Sicily; and Tritons and water nymphs frolicked around galleys ready to set forth on mother-of-pearl seas.

Once this proud overture was passed, though, the house was all grace and charm, or rather gentleness veiled its pride as courtesy does that of an aristocrat. There was a library, its books shut inside cupboards of that decorative eighteenth-century Sicilian style called "Monastic," not unlike the more florid Venetian but cruder and less sweetened. There was nearly every work of the Enlightenment in tawny leather and gilt binding: *L'Encyclopédie,* Fontenelle, Helvétius, Voltaire in Kehle's great edition (if Maria Carolina read that, what must she have thought?); then *Victoires et conquêtes,* a collection of Napoleonic bulletins and campaign reports which were my delight in the long silence-filled summer afternoons as I read them sprawled on one of those enormous poufs which occupied the center of the ballroom. An odd library, in fact, if one considers that it had been formed by the Prince

Niccolò who was a reactionary. Also to be found there were bound collections of the satirical journals of the Risorgimento, *Il Fischietto* and *Lo Spirito Folletto,* some exquisite editions of Don Quixote, of La Fontaine, that rare history of Napoleon with Norvins' charming illustrations (a book I still have); and among moderns the complete works, or almost, of Zola, whose yellow covers showed up glaringly on that mellow background, and a few other lesser novels; but there was also *I Malavoglia,* with an autographed dedication.

I do not know whether I have managed so far to convey the idea that I was a boy who loved solitude, who liked the company of things more than of people. This being the case it will easily be understood how ideal for me was life at Santa Margherita. I would wander through the vast ornate house as in an enchanted wood. A wood with no hidden dragons, full of happy marvels, even in the jesting names of the rooms: the "aviary room," its walls covered in rough crinkled white silk, on which amid infinite festoons of flowering branches glittered tiny multicolored birds painted in by hand; the *"wistiti* room," where on similar tropical trees swung sly and hairy monkeys; "the rooms of Ferdinando," which evoked at first in me the idea of a fair smiling uncle of mine, but which had actually kept this name because they had been the private apartments of the cruel and jocular *Re Nasone,** as was also shown by the huge Empire *lit-bateau,* whose mattress was covered in a kind of morocco leather casing, apparently used on royal beds instead of an under blanket: green morocco leather, closely stamped with the triple gilt lilies of Bourbon, and looking like an enormous book. The walls were covered in silk of paler green, with vertical stripes, one shiny and one mat with tiny lines, just like that in the green drawing room of our house in Palermo. Then in the "tapestry hall," the only one with some sinister association later, hung eight big tapestries on subjects taken from *Gerusalemme Liberata.* In one of these, representing an equestrian joust between Tancredi and Argante, one of the two horses had a strangely human look which I was to link in my mind later with Poe's "House of the Metzingersteins." This particular tapestry, actually, is still in my possession.

The evenings, oddly enough, we always spent in the ballroom, an apartment in the center of the first floor

* King Ferdinand I & IV of the Two Sicilies.

with eight balconies looking out over the piazza and four over the first courtyard. It was reminiscent of the ballroom of our house in Palermo; here, too, gold was the dominating note of the room. The walls, on the other hand, were pale green, almost entirely covered with hand-embroidered flowers and golden leaves, and the bases of pillars and the shutters vast as front doors were covered completely in dull gold-leaf with decorations in brighter gold. And when on winter evenings (we actually spent two winters at Santa Margherita, which my mother was loath to leave) we sat in front of the central fireplace, by the glow of a few oil lamps whose light picked out capriciously a few flowers on the walls and flames in the shutters, we seemed to be enclosed in some magician's cave. I can definitely place the date of one of these evenings because I remember that newspapers were brought in announcing the fall of Port Arthur.

These evenings were not always restricted to the family alone; in fact they seldom were. My mother wanted to keep up her parents' tradition of being on cordial terms with the local notabilities, and many of these would dine with us in turn, while twice a week everyone met to play *scopone* in the ballroom. My mother had known them

74

since childhood and liked them all; to me they seemed, what perhaps they were not, good people without exception. Among them there was a native of Palermo forced by his wretched financial condition to emigrate to Santa Margherita, where he had a tiny house and an even tinier patch of ground; he was a great hunter, had been a close friend of my grandfather's, and enjoyed particularly favorable treatment; I think he used to lunch with us every day and was the only one to call my mother "*tu*," which she returned with a respectful "*lei*"; he was a straight, thin old man, with blue eyes and long white sprouting mustaches, distinguished and even elegant in his threadbare clothes of good cut. I suspect now that he may have been a bastard of the Cutò family, some uncle of my mother's in fact. He would play the piano and tell wonderful tales of shooting out in the wilds and woods with my grandfather, of the prodigious acumen of his hunting dogs (Diana and Furetta), and of alarming but ever innocuous encounters with the brigand bands of Leone and Capraro. Then there was XX, a local landowner of insatiable vivacity, looked up to as a great *viveur* in the town, as he spent two months of every year in Palermo at a hotel, which was considered "fast."

75

There was an old clerk who talked of nothing but Viterbo ("You must realize, Duchess, that Viterbo is almost Rome"), where he had spent a few months on service. There was XXX, with his big rubicund face and mutton-chop whiskers à la Franz Josef, who lived with a mad relative (when one knows a Sicilian village well one discovers innumerable lunatics); there was the schoolmaster with a Mosaic beard; and another big landowner, the real type of a rustic lordling, obtuse and gross; Giorgio di Giuseppe, the intellectual of the company, from beneath whose windows passers-by at night heard Chopin's nocturnes played by him on the pianoforte; XXXX, hugely fat and full of fun; an engineer from Catania with a little black beard, who had studied in Paris and often spoke of the Rue Daru, where he had had the oddest adventures; another, very old and almost wholly peasant; young Fefè, a great trencherman; and many others who were seen more rarely.

It will be noticed these were one and all men. Wives, daughters, sisters stayed at home, both because women in the country (in 1905–14) did not pay visits, and also because their husbands, fathers, and brothers did not want them around. My mother and father would go and visit

them once a season, and with one, famous for her gas-
tronomic arts, they would even sometimes take luncheon; sometimes, after a complex system of signals and
warnings, she would send over by a small boy, who came
galloping across the piazza under the broiling sun, an
immense tureen full of macaroni done with barley in the
Sicilian mode with chopped meat, eggplant, and basil,
which was, I remember, truly a dish fit for rustic and
primigenial gods. The boy had precise orders to set this
on the dining table when we were already sitting down,
and before leaving, he would say, *"'A signura raccu-
mannu: u cascavaddu"* ("The Signora recommends:
caciocavallo cheese"), an injunction perhaps sage but
never obeyed.

V

THE GARDEN

In the center of the courtyard, to the left of stables and riding school, stood two high pillars in porous yellow stone, adorned with masks and scrolls, which opened onto a flight of steps leading down into the garden. They were a short flight (a dozen or so steps in all), but in that space the baroque architect had found ways of expressing a freakish and whimsical turn of mind, alternating high and low steps, twisting motifs together in most unexpected ways, creating superfluous little landings with niches and benches so as to produce in this small space a variety of possible joinings and separations, of brusque rejections and affectionate reconciliations, which imparted to the staircase the atmosphere of a lovers' tiff.

The garden, like so many others in Sicily, was designed on a level lower than the house, I think so that advantage could be taken of a spring welling up there. It was very large, and when seen from a window of the house perfectly regular in its complicated system of alleys and paths. It was all planted out with ilex and araucaria, the alleys bordered with myrtle hedges; and in the furnace of summer, when the jet of the spring dwindled, it was a paradise of parched scents of origan and catmint, as are so many gardens in Sicily that seem made to delight the nose rather than the eyes.

The long alleys surrounding it on all four sides were the only straight ones in the whole garden, for in the rest the designer (who must surely have been the whimsical architect of the stairs) had multiplied twists, turns, mazes, and corridors, contributing to give it that tone of graceful mystery which enveloped the whole house. All these cross-alleys, however, came out eventually onto a big central clearing, the one where the spring had been found; this, now enclosed in an ornate prison, lightened with its spurts a great fountain in the center of which, on an islet of artificial ruins, a disheveled and ungirt Goddess of Abundance poured torrents of water into a deep basin forever crossed by friendly ripples. It was bounded by a balustrade, surmounted here and there by Tritons and Nereids sculptured in the act of diving with movements that were disordered in each individual statue but fused into a scenic whole. All around the fountain were stone benches darkened by centuries-old moss.

But for a child the garden was brimful of surprises. In a corner was a big thicket filled with cacti and rare shrubs, the kingdom of Nino, head gardener and my great friend, he too red-haired like so many at Santa Margherita, perhaps derived from the Norman Filangeri. There was a bamboo thicket, growing thick and sturdy around a secondary fountain, in the shade of which was an open space for games, with a swing from which long before my time Pietro Scalea, later Minister of War, fell and broke his arm. In one of the side alleys, embedded in the wall, was a big cage destined at one time for monkeys, in which a girl cousin and I shut ourselves one day, a Sunday morning when the garden was open to the townsfolk, who stopped in mute amazement to gaze, uncertainly, at these dressed-up simians. There was a dolls' house, built for the diversion of my mother and her four sisters, made of red brick, with window frames in *pietra serena*; now, with its roof and floors fallen in, it was the only disconsolate corner of the big garden, the remainder of which Nino kept in admirable order with every tree well pruned, every alley yellow-pebbled, every bush clipped.

Once in two weeks or so a cart came up from the nearby Belice with a big barrel full of eels, which were unloaded into the secondary fountain (the one of the bamboos), that served as a fishpond to which the cook sent for eels to be scooped out with little nets according to needs of the kitchen.

Everywhere at corners of alleys rose figures of obscure gods, usually noseless; and as in every self-respecting Eden there was a serpent hidden in the shadows, in the shape of some castor-oil shrubs (lovely in other ways with their green leaves bordered in red) which one day gave me a nasty surprise when, crushing the berries of a fine vermilion bunch, I recognized upon the air the smell of the oil that, at that happy age, was the only real shadow on my life.

A garden, I have said, full of surprises. But the whole of Santa Margherita was that, full of the gay unexpected.

One would open a door on a passage and glimpse a perspective of rooms dim in the shade of half-shut blinds,
their walls covered with French prints representing Bona-
parte's campaigns in Italy; at the top of the stairs leading
to the second floor was a door that was almost invisible,
so narrow was it and flush with the wall, and behind this
was a big room crammed with old pictures hung right
up to the very top of the walls, as in prints of the Paris
Salon in the eighteenth century. One of the ancestral portraits in the first room was hinged, and behind lay my
uncle's gun rooms, for he was a great hunter.

The trophies shut in glass cabinets were local only:
pheasants, disconsolate-looking woodcocks, moorhens
from the Belice; but a big bench with scales, little measures for preparing cartridges, glass-fronted cupboards full
of multicolored cartridge cases, colored prints showing
more dangerous adventures (I can still see a bearded ex-
plorer in white fleeing screaming before the charge of a
greenish rhinoceros), all these were enchantments to an
adolescent. On the walls also hung prints and photographs
of hunting dogs, pointers and setters, showing the calm
of all canine faces. The guns were ranged in big racks,

ticketed with numbers corresponding to a register in which were recorded the shots fired from each. It was from one of these guns, I think a lady's, with two richly damascened barrels, that I fired, in the garden, the first and last shots of my sporting career: one of the bearded keepers forced me to fire on some innocent redbreasts; two fell, unfortunately, with blood on their tepid gray plumage; and as they were still quivering the keeper wrung their necks with his fingers.

In spite of my readings of *Victoires et conquêtes,* and *"l'épée de l'intrépide général rougie du sang des ennemis de l'Empire,"* this scene horrified me: apparently I only like blood when metamorphosed into printer's ink. I went straight to my father, to whose orders this slaughter of the Innocents was due, and said that never again would I fire on anyone.

Ten years later I was to kill a Bosnian with a pistol and who knows how many other Christians by shellfire. But it never made a tenth of the impression on me that those two wretched redbreasts did.

I held out my smeared hand to my well-loved poodle Tom who was following me, and I can still see the kind but reproachful way with which he raised half his black lip, as well-brought-up dogs do when they want to show their disgust without offending their masters.

There was also the "carriage room," a great, dark chamber, in which stood two enormous eighteenth-century *carrosses,* one gala, all gilt and glass, with doors on whose panels, against a yellow background, were painted pastoral scenes in *vernis Martin;* its seats, for at least six persons, were of faded taffeta; the other, a traveling carriage, was olive green with gilt edgings and coats of arms on the door panels. Beneath the seats there were lined cupboards intended, I think, for provisions on a journey, but now containing only a solitary silver dish.

Then there was the "children's kitchen" with a miniature range and a set of copper cooking implements in proportion, which my grandmother had installed in a vain attempt to inveigle her daughters into learning to cook.

And then there were the church and the theater, with the fairy-tale passages by which they were reached, but of those I will speak later.

Amid all these splendors I slept in a completely bare room overlooking the garden, called the "pink room" because of the colors of its varnished plaster; on one side was a dressing room with a strange oval brass bath raised on four high wooden legs. I remember the baths which I was made to take in water that had starch dissolved in it or bran in a little bag from which when wet came a scented, milky drip: *bains de son,* bran baths, traces of which can be found in memoirs of the Second Empire, a habit which had evidently been handed on to my mother by my grandmother.

In a room near by, identical to mine but blue, slept successively German governesses and French *mesdemoiselles.* At my bedhead hung a kind of Louis Seize showcase in white wood, enclosing three ivory statuettes of the Holy Family on a crimson background. This case has been miraculously salvaged and now hangs at the bedhead of the room on which I sleep at my cousin Piccolo's villa at Capo d'Orlando. In that villa, too, I find again not only the "Holy Family" of my infancy, but a trace, faint certainly but unmistakable, of my childhood; and so I love going there.

V I

THE CHURCH AND THE THEATER

Them was also the church, which was then the cathedral of Santa Margherita. From the coach room one turned left and, up a few steps, reached a wide passage ending in a kind of schoolroom with benches, blackboards, and relief maps, where my mother and aunts had done their lessons as children.

It was at Santa Margherita, at the not-so-tender age of eight, that I was taught to read. To begin with others read aloud to me; on alternate days—that is, Tuesdays, Thursdays, and Saturdays—"Sacred History" and a kind of potted version of the Bible and the Gospels; and on

Mondays, Wednesdays, and Fridays, classical mythology.
So I acquired a "solid" knowledge of both these dis-
ciplines; I am still capable of saying how many, and who,
were the brothers of Joseph and of finding my way among
the complicated family squabbles of the Atrides. Before
I learned to read for myself my grandmother was forced
by her own goodness to read aloud for an hour out of *The
Queen of the Caribbean* by Salgari; and I can still see
her trying hard not to fall asleep as she read about the
prowess of the Black Pirate and the swashbuckling of
Carmaux.

Eventually it was decided that this religious, classic,
and adventuresome culture, vicariously imparted, could
not last much longer, and that I was to be handed over to
Donna Carmela, an elementary schoolmistress at Santa
Margherita. Nowadays elementary schoolmistresses are
smart, lively young ladies, who chatter about Pestalozzi's
and James's pedagogic studies and want to be called *"Pro-
fessoressa."* In 1905, in Sicily, an elementary schoolmistress
was an old woman more than half peasant, with her
spectacled head wrapped up in a black shawl; but actually this one was a most expert teacher, and within
two months I knew how to read and write and had lost

87

my doubts about double consonants and accented sylla-bles. For whole weeks, in the "blue room" separated from my pink room only by the passage, I had to carry out sibilated dictations—si-bi-la-ted dic-ta-tions—and repeat dozens of times, *"di, do, da, fe, fa, fu, qui* and *qua* don't take an accent." Blessed labors!

When I had learned to write Italian my mother taught me to write French; I already spoke it and had often been to Paris and in France, but it was now that I learned to read French. I can still see my mother sitting with me at a desk, writing slowly and very clearly *le chien, le chat, le cheval* in the columns of an exercise book with a shiny blue cover, and teaching me that "ch" in French is like "sc" in Italian, "as in *scirocco* and *sciacca*," she would say. From then on until my school days, I spent all my after-noons in my grandparents' apartments at Via Lampedusa, reading behind a screen. At five o'clock my grandfather would call me into his study to give me my afternoon refreshment—a hunk of bread and a large glass of cold water. It has remained my favorite drink ever since.

On the right of the carriage room, between two white console tables, was a big yellow door. From this one entered a small oblong room, its chairs and various tables loaded with images of saints; I can still see a big china dish in the middle of which lay the head of St. John the Baptist, life-size, with blood coagulated in the bottom. From this room one entered a gallery at the level of a high first story, looking straight onto the High Altar, which was surrounded by a superb railing of flowery gilt. In this gallery were *prie-dieux,* chairs, and innumerable rosaries, and from it every Sunday at eleven we heard High Mass without excessive fervor. The church itself was a fine spacious one, I remember, in Empire style, with large, ugly frescoes in white stucco work on the ceiling, as in the Olivella church in Palermo which, though smaller, it was not unlike.

From this same carriage room which, I now remember, was a kind of revolving stage for the least frequented part of the house, one penetrated to the right into a series of passages, cubbyholes, and staircases that gave one a sense of having no outlet—like certain dreams—and eventually reached the corridor of the theater. This was a real and proper theater, with two tiers each of eleven boxes, as well as a main box, and, of course, orchestra seats. The auditorium, capable of holding at least three hundred people, was all white and gold, with its seats and the walls of boxes lined in very light blue velvet. The style was Louis Seize, restrained and elegant. In the center was the equivalent of the royal box, that is, our box, surmounted by an enormous shield of gilt wood, containing the belled cross set on a double-headed eagle's breast. And the drop curtain, rather late in date, represented the defense of Antioch by Riccardo Filangeri (a defense which, according to Grousset, was far less heroic than the painter gave one to believe).

The auditorium was lit by gilt oil lamps set on brackets projecting under the first tier of boxes.

The best of it was that this theater (which of course also had a public entrance from the piazza) was often used.

Every now and again a company of actors would arrive; these were strolling players who, generally in summer, moved on carts from one village to the other, staying two or three days in each to give performances. In Santa Margherita, where there was a proper theater, they stayed longer, two or three weeks.

At ten in the morning the leading actor would call in frock coat and top hat to ask for permission to perform in the theater; he would be received by my father or, in his absence, by my mother, who of course gave permission, refused any rent (or rather made a contract for a token rental of fifty *centisimi* for the two weeks), and also paid a subscription for our own box. After which the leading actor left, to return half an hour later and request a loan of furniture. These companies traveled, in fact, with a few bits of painted scenery but no stage furniture, which would have been too costly and inconvenient to carry about. The furniture was granted, and in the evening we would recognize our armchairs, tables, and coat hangers on the stage (they were not our best, I'm sorry to say). They were handed back punctually at the moment of departure, sometimes so garishly revarnished that we had to ask other companies to desist from this well-intentioned practice. Once the leading lady also called on us, a fat, good-natured Ferrarese of about thirty who was to interpret the *Dame aux camélias* for the farewell night. Finding her own wardrobe unsuitable for the solemnity of the occasion she came to ask my mother for an evening dress: and so the Lady of the Camellias appeared in a very low-cut robe of Nile green covered in silver spangles.

These companies wandering around country villages have now vanished, which is a pity. The scenery was primitive, the acting obviously bad; but they played with gusto and fire and their "presence" was certainly more lifelike than are the pallid shades of fifth-rate films now shown in the same villages.

Every night there was a play, and the repertoire was most extensive; the whole of nineteenth-century drama passed on that stage: Scribe, Rovetta, Sardou, Giacometti, and Torelli. Once there was even a *Hamlet,* the first time in fact that I ever heard it. And the audience, partly of peasants, were attentive and warm in their applause. At Santa Margherita, at least, these companies did good business, with theater and furniture free and their draught horses put up and foddered in our stables.

I used to attend every night, except on one night of the season called "black night," when some French *pochade,* reputed indecent, was shown. Next day our local friends came to report on this libertine performance, and were usually very disappointed as they had expected something much more indecent.

I enjoyed it all enormously, and so did my parents. The better companies at the end of their season were offered a kind of rustic garden party with a simple but abundant buffet out in the garden, which cheered up the stomachs, often empty I fear, of those excellent strolling players.

But already in the last year that I spent a long period at Santa Margherita, 1921, companies of actors no longer came, and instead flickering films were shown. The war had killed off, with all the rest, these poor and picturesque wandering companies which had their own artistic merits and were, I have an idea, the training school of many a great Italian actor and actress of the nineteenth century, Duse among others.

VII

EXCURSIONS

O F ALL THE WALKS around Santa Margherita, that toward Montevago was our most frequent, for it ran level, was the right length (about two miles each way), and had a definite if not attractive goal: Montevago itself.

Then there was a walk in the opposite direction, on the main road toward Misilbesi; one passed under a huge umbrella pine and then over the Dragonara bridge, surrounded unexpectedly by thick, wild verdure which reminded me of scenes from Ariosto as I imagined them at that period from Doré's illustrations. On reaching

Misilbesi, a desolate crossroads marked by a pustulous old house with three dusty and deserted roads that seemed to be leading to Hades rather than to Sciacca or Sambuca, we generally returned by carriage, as our usual four miles were greatly exceeded.

The carriage had followed us at walking pace, stopping every now and again so as not to overtake us and then rejoining us unhurriedly; phases of silence and of disappearance alternating according to the turns of the road, before we were caught up with a clatter.

In autumn our walks had as goal a vineyard, where we would sit on stones and eat sweet mottled grapes (wine grapes, for in 1905 table grapes were scarcely ever cultivated in our region), after which we entered a room in semidarkness; at the end of it a lusty young man was jerking like a madman inside a barrel, his feet squashing the grapes whose greenish juice could be seen flowing down a wooden channel, while the air was filled with a heavy smell of must.

*Dance, and provincial noise, and sunburnt mirth.**

* In English in the original. This is a play on a line from Keats's "Ode to a Nightingale":
    Dance, and Provençal song, and sunburnt mirth.

No, no *mirth* at all; in Sicily there was none, there never is even now during work: the *stornelli*-singing of Tuscan girls at vintage, the Livornian threshing punctuated by feasting, song, and love-making, are things unknown; all work is *n'a camurría,* a blasphemous contravention of the eternal repose granted by the gods to our "lotus-eaters."

On rainy autumn afternoons our walk was confined to the public gardens. These were set at the northern limit of the town, on a hillside overlooking the great valley which is probably the main east-west axis of Sicily and is certainly one of its few outstanding geographical features.

These gardens had been given to the municipality by my grandfather and were of quite infinite melancholy; a longish alley bordered by young cypresses and old ilexes led to a bare open space facing a small shrine of the Madonna of Trapani, with a flower bed of parched yellow bamboos in the middle and on the left a kind of kiosk temple with a round dome from which to gaze at the view.

And it was worth gazing at. Opposite stretched a vast

13. *The church at Palma di Montechiaro, founded by the Saint-Duke in the seventeenth century.*

14. The convent at Palma di Montechiaro, originally the palace of the Tomasi. A visit paid here by the author in 1955 is said to have directly inspired an important scene in The Leopard.

15. *The Saint-Duke. Giulio Tomasi, Duke of Palma, who "scourged himself alone in sight of his God and his estates."*

16. *A view from the Saint-Duke's balcony which "overlooked the yellow expanse of estate after estate."*

range of low mountains, all yellow from reaping, with blackish patches of burnt stubble, so that one had a vivid impression of a monstrous crouching beast. On the flanks of this lioness or hyena (according to the eye of the beholder) could just be made out villages whose grayish-yellow stone was scarcely distinguishable from the background: Poggioreale, Contessa, Salaparuta, Gibellina, Santa Ninfa, all weltering in poverty and dog days, and in ignorance against which they never reacted with even the faintest of flickers.

The little shrine at the other side of the open space in the gardens was a target for anticlerical manifestatos by Santa Margherita's law students, there on vacation. Often could be seen written up in pencil strophes from Carducci's "Hymn to Satan": *"Salute, o Santana, o ribellione, o forza vindice della ragione."* * And when my mother (who knew the "Hymn to Satan" by heart and whose lack of admiration for it was due to æsthetic reasons alone) next morning sent Nino our gardener to put a coat of whitewash over the modestly sacrilegious verses, others appeared two days later: *"Ti scomunico, o prete, vate di*

* "Greetings, O Satan, O rebellion, O avenging force of reason."

lutti e d'ire" * and other volleys which the good Giosuè†
thought it his duty to discharge against citizen Mastai.‡

On the slope below the kiosk could be gathered capers,
which I did regularly at the risk of breaking my neck;
and around there also, it seems, were to be found those
Spanish flies whose pulverized heads make such a potent
aphrodisiac. I was sure at the time that these flies were
there; but whom I heard this from, or when or how,
remains a mystery. Never in my life, at any rate, have I
set eyes on Spanish flies, dead or alive, whole or in powder.

Such were our daily, not very exacting walks. Then
there were longer, more complicated ones, our excursions.

The chief excursion of all was that to La Venaría, a
hunting lodge on a spur just before Montevago. This
was an excursion always made with local guests twice or
so in a season, and was never without an element of
comedy. A decision would be reached: "Next Sunday,
lunch at Venaría." And in the morning off we would set
at ten o'clock, ladies in carriages, men on donkeys. Al-

* "I excommunicate you, O priest, bearer of mourning and wrath."
† Giosuè Carducci (1835-1907) classicist poet; considered national poet
of modern Italy.
‡ Pope Pius IX.

though all or almost all the men owned horses or at least mules, the use of donkeys was traditional; the only rebel was my father, who got around the difficulty by declaring himself to be the one person capable of driving, on those roads, the dogcart, conveying the ladies and bearing also, in the dog cages secreted under the box, the bottles and cakes for the guests' luncheon.

Amid laughter and jest the company would take the road to Montevago. In the middle of the dusty group was the dogcart in which my mother, with Anna or whichever Mademoiselle was with us or with some other lady, tried to shelter from the dust with gray veils of almost Moslem thickness; around would prance the donkeys (or rather *"i sciucche,"* for in Sicilian donkeys are almost always feminine, like ships in English). There were real falls, genuine donkeys' mutinies, and false falls due to love of the picturesque. We crossed Montevago, arousing vocal protests from every dog in the place, reached the Dàgali bridge, branched off the road, and began climbing.

The avenue was really grandiose; about three hundred yards long, it went straight up toward the top of the hill, bordered on each side by a double row of cypresses; not adolescent cypresses like those of San Guido, but great trees almost a hundred years old, whose thick branches spread in every season their austere scent.* The rows of trees were interrupted every now and again by sets of benches, and once by a fountain with a great mask emitting water at intervals. Under the odorous shade we climbed toward La Venaría, bathed in full sunshine high above.

It was a hunting lodge built at the end of the eighteenth century, considered "tiny," though actually it must have had at least twenty rooms. Built on top of the hill, on the opposite side to the one by which we approached, it looked sheer across the valley, the same valley to be seen from the public gardens, which from higher up seemed vast and even desolate.

Cooks had left that morning at seven and had already prepared everything; when a boy lookout announced the group's approach they thrust into the ovens their famous timbales of macaroni *alla Talleyrand* (the only macaroni which keeps some time), so that when we arrived we had scarcely time to wash our hands before going straight

* Now felled by later owners.

out onto the terrace, where two tables had been laid in the open air.

Huge cold fish with mayonnaise sauce followed, then stuffed turkey and avalanches of potatoes. One might expect strokes from overeating. A fat guest nearly did pass out once: but a pailful of cold water in his face and a prudent nap in a shady room saved him. Next, all was put to rights by the arrival of one of those iced cakes at which Marsala, the cook, was a past master. Wines, as always in sober Sicily, were of no importance. The guests expected them, of course, and liked their glasses filled to the brim ("no collars" they would shout to the footmen), but of their collarless glasses they emptied one, at the most two.

After dusk we descended homeward.

I have spoken of excursions in the plural; actually our only real excursion, thinking it over, was that to La Venaría. In the first years there were others, of which, however, I have kept only rather vague memories; though the word "vague" is not quite exact; a better phrase would be "difficult to describe." The visual impression has remained vivid in my mind but was not then linked to any word. We must have been out to Sciacca, for instance, to lunch with friends when I was six or seven years old; but of the luncheon, the people we met, the journey, I have no memory at all. On the other hand, of Sciacca itself, or rather of its promenade above the sea, such a photographic, complete, and precise image has remained stamped on my mind that when I returned there a couple of years ago, for the first time after nearly fifty years, I was easily able to compare the scene under my eyes with the old one that had remained in my mind, and note the many similarities and the few differences.

As always, my memories are particularly memories of light: at Sciacca I see a very blue, almost black, sea glinting furiously beneath the midday sun, in one of those skies of high Sicilian summer which are misty with heat, a balustrade over a sheer drop to the sea, a kind of arcade to the left of which was a café—which is still there.

Looming skies with scudding rain clouds, on the other hand, remind me of a small country place near Catania, set on a steep hillside reached by a zigzagging road which, I don't know why, horses had to ascend at a gallop. I see a landau with dusty blue cushions (the very fact they were blue showed that the carriage was not our own but hired), my mother sitting in a corner, panic-stricken herself but trying to reassure me, while beside us the trees whirled past and vanished with the speed of wind, and the coachman's incitements mingled with whip cracks and frenzied tingling of collar bells (no, that carriage was certainly not ours).

Of the house where we were going I retain a memory which I can now say was its gentlemanly but poverty-stricken air; obviously I did not formulate this economic-social judgment at the time, but I can say it in all serenity now, examining the mental photograph recently retrieved from the archives of memory.

Guests at Santa Margherita were few; there were no automobiles then, or rather three or four at most in the whole of Sicily, and the ghastly state of the roads induced the owners of the *rarae aves* to use them only in towns.

I have a very vivid memory of XYZ. He belonged to a good local family, feudatories of the Filangeri; for the Filangeri had the right, very rare and much envied, of investing with a barony a total of two of their own vassals in every generation. The XYZ (who had been judges of the High Court way back under the Empire) had been granted this privilege, and my grandmother even used to call them "very first vassals among my vassals."

XYZ then gave me the impression of being an old man; actually he could not have been more than forty. He was very tall, very thin, very shortsighted; in spite of his spectacles, which were a *pince-nez* and had extraordinarily thick lenses, squashing down his nose with their weight, he used to walk bent in the hope of recognizing at least a vague shadow of his surroundings.

A good, sensitive person, well liked and of no great intelligence, he had dedicated his life to (and spent the greater part of his fortune on) trying to be "a man of fashion." And from the point of view of dress he had certainly succeeded: never have I seen a man with a wardrobe more sober, better cut, or less showy than his. He had been one of the moths drawn by the glamorous glow of the Florios, a moth who, after many a dizzy pirouette, dropped onto the tablecloth with burnt-out wings. He had been more than once to Paris with the Florios and even put up at the Ritz; and of Paris (the Paris of the *boites,* of luxurious brothels, of high-priced elegance) he had preserved a dazzled memory which made him rather like the engineer I have mentioned before; with the difference that the engineer's memories were based on the Latin Quarter and the Polytechnic. They were not on very good terms, XYZ and the engineer, perhaps because of their rivalry in disputing the favors of the *Ville Lumière*.

Poor XYZ became almost blind and utterly destitute before he died not so many years ago. My mother, who went to visit him until the end, would return much affected by his being so bent that when sitting in his armchair his face was eight inches from the floor, and to talk to him she had had to sit on a cushion right on the floor itself.

VIII

THE PINK DINING ROOM

B<small>UT I REALIZE</small> that I have forgotten to mention the dining room, which was singular for various reasons; singular particularly for existing at all; in an eighteenth-century house it was very rare, I think, to have a room set apart as a dining room: at that time people dined in any drawing room, changing continually, as in fact I still do now.

But there was one at Santa Margherita. Not very big, it could hold about twenty chairs comfortably. It looked out over two balconies onto the second courtyard. The doors were white, Louis Seize, and had big panels with decorations in relief, gilt, of a greenish dull gold. From the ceiling hung a Murano chandelier, whose grayish glass showed up the color of floral designs.

Prince Alessandro, who arranged this room, had thought up the idea of asking a local artist to paint on the walls pictures of himself and his family while actually eating their meals. These were large pictures on canvas, completely covering a wall from floor to ceiling with life-size figures.

One showed breakfast: the Prince and Princess, he in green hunting clothes, boots, and a hat, she in white *déshabillé* but wearing jewels, sitting at a small table intent on taking chocolate, served by a little Negro slave in a turban. She was holding out a biscuit to an impatient hound, he raising toward his mouth a big blue cup decorated with flowers. Another picture represented a picnic: a number of ladies and gentlemen were sitting around a tablecloth spread in a field and covered with splendid-looking pastries and grass-plaited bottles; in the background could be seen a fountain, and the trees were young and low. This, I think, must have been the actual garden of Santa Margherita just after it was planted.

A third picture, the biggest, represented a formal dinner

party with the gentlemen in very curly wigs and the ladies in full evening dress. The Princess was wearing a delicious robe of silver-pink broché silk, with a dog collar around her neck and a great parure of rubies on her bosom. Footmen in full livery and cordons were entering bearing high dishes elaborately decorated.

There were another two pictures, but I can only remember the subject of one of them, for it was always facing me: this was the children's afternoon refreshment. Two little girls of ten and twelve years of age, powdered and tightly laced into their pointed bodices, sat facing a boy of about fifteen, dressed in an orange-colored suit with black facings and carrying a rapier, and an old lady in black (certainly the governess); all were eating large ices of an odd pink color, maybe of cinnamon, rising in sharp cones from long glass goblets.

Another of the oddities of the house was the table centerpiece in the dining room. This was a large fixed silver ornament, surmounted by Neptune who threatened the guests with his trident, while beside him an Amphitrite eyed him with a hint of malice. The whole was set on a rock rising in the middle of a silver basin, surrounded by dolphins and marine monsters squirting water from their mouths through some machinery hidden in a central part of the table. It was all very gay and grand, but had the inconvenience of requiring tablecloths with a large hole cut out of the middle for Neptune. (The holes were hidden by flowers or leaves.) There were no cupboards, but four big console tables covered with pink marble; and the general tone of the room was pink—in the marble, in the Princess's pink dress, in the big picture, and also in the chair coverings which were pink too, not old but of delicate hue.

Near the dining room, in another apartment, were enormous cupboards of yellow wood, the keys of which had been lost; not even the administrator knew where they were, and when one said that there was no more to be said. After a long hesitation the blacksmith was eventually called and the doors were opened. The cupboards contained bed linen, dozens and dozens of sheets and pillowcases, enough for an entire hotel (there were already overwhelming quantities of these in known cupboards); others contained blankets of real wool scattered with pepper and camphor; still others table linen, small, large, or outsize damask tablecloths, all with that hole in the middle. And between one layer and another of this home

109

treasure were placed little tulle sacks of lavender flowers now in dust. But the most interesting cupboard was one containing writing materials of the eighteenth century; it was a little smaller than the others, and heaped with great sheets of pure rag letter-paper, bundles of quill pens tied neatly in dozens, red and blue sealing wafers, and very long sticks of sealing wax.

As can be seen, the house of Santa Margherita was a kind of eighteenth-century Pompeii, all miraculously preserved intact: a rare thing always, but almost unique in Sicily, which from poverty and neglect is the most destructive of countries. I do not know what were the exact causes of this durability: perhaps the fact that my maternal grandfather spent long years there between 1820 and 1840 in a kind of exile imposed on him by the Bourbon kings as a result of a misdemeanor on the Marine Parade at Palermo,* or perhaps the passionate care which my grandmother took of it: certainly the fact of her finding a unique administrator, the only one who, to my knowledge, was not a thief.

He was still alive in my time: a kind of dwarf with a long white beard, living together with an incredibly

* Driving his carriage stark naked.

large fat wife in one of the many apartments attached to the house with a separate entrance.

Marvels were recounted of his care and scrupulosity: how, when the house was empty, he went through it every night with lantern in hand to check that all the windows were shut and doors bolted; how he allowed only his wife to wash the precious china; how after a reception (in my grandmother's time) he checked the screws under every chair; how during the winter he spent entire days surveying squads of cleaners polishing and ordering every single object, however out of the way, in that gigantic house. In spite of his age and anything but youthful aspect his wife was very jealous of him; and ever and again news would reach us of terrific scenes which she made due to her suspicion of his paying too much attention to the charms of some young maidservant. I know for certain that a number of times he protested most vigorously to my mother about her overspending; advice, it goes without saying, unheeded, and maybe ill treated.

His death coincided with the rapid and sudden end of this loveliest of lovely country homes. May these lines which no one will read be a homage to its unblemished memory.

III

The Professor and the Mermaid

A STORY

[*January, 1957*]

In the late autumn of that year, 1938, I had a bad fit of the spleen. I was living in Turin at the time, and my tart No. 1, while groping about in my pockets for an odd fifty-lire note as I slept, had also found a letter from tart No. 2, which in spite of spelling mistakes left no doubts about the nature of our relationship.

My awakening had been immediate and stormy. The little flat in Via Peyron echoed with vernacular tantrums; there was even an attempt to scratch my eyes out, which I only evaded by giving a slight twist to the dear girl's left wrist. This fully justified act of self-defense put an end to the scene, but to our idyll too. She flung her clothes on, thrust into her bag powderpuff, lipstick, hanky, and the fifty-lire *causa mali tanti,* hissed the Torinese for "swine!" into my face thrice, and left. Never had she been so attractive as during that quarter of an hour's raging. From my window I watched her go out and move off into the morning mist, tall, slim, wrapped in reconquered poise.

Never again did I set eyes on her, as I never set eyes on a black cashmere pullover of great cost, which had the fatal quality of being styled for either male or female use. All she left me, on the bed, were two of those small, twisted, so-called "invisible" hairpins.

That same afternoon I had an appointment with No. 2 at a confectioner's in the Piazza Carlo Felice. At the little round table in the western corner of the inner room which was "ours," I saw, not the chestnut locks of the girl who was now more than ever desirable, but the sly features of Tonino, a young brother of hers aged twelve who had just finished guzzling down a cup of chocolate with a double portion of whipped cream. As I drew near he got up with the usual Torinese urbanity. *"Monsú,"* he said, "Pinotta's not coming. She told me to give you this note. *Cerea, monsú.*" And off he went, taking with him two brioches left on the dish. In the ivory-colored missive I was notified of summary dismissal due to my infamy and "southern dishonesty." Obviously No. 1 had traced and incited No. 2, and I was left recumbent between two stools.

In twelve hours I had lost two girls who were usefully complementary as well as a pullover I liked, and had also to pay that infernal Tonino's cake bill. My very Sicilian self-respect was humiliated: I had been made a fool of; and I decided to abandon the world and its pomps awhile.

For this period of retirement I could have found no place more suitable that the café in Via Po where I began spending every free moment alone and always went in the evening after my work on the paper. It was a kind of Hades peopled by bloodless shades of lieutenant colonels, magistrates, and professors. These insubstantial apparitions would play draughts or dominoes, immersed in a light dimmed, during the day, by arcades and clouds and at night by huge green shades on the chandeliers; no voices were ever raised lest too loud a sound disturb their tenuous woof. A most suitable Limbo.

Like the creature of habit that I am I used always to sit at the same corner table, carefully designed to offer customers a maximum of discomfort. On my left a pair of ghostly senior officers would be playing *tric-trac* with a couple of phantoms from the Court of Appeal; military and judicial dice slithered listlessly from the leather cup. On my right always sat an elderly gentleman muffled in an old overcoat with a mangy astrakhan collar. He read foreign magazines ceaselessly, smoked Tuscan cheroots, and spat a great deal; every now and again he shut up his magazines and seemed to be following some memory in the volutes of smoke. Then he would begin reading and spitting again. He had hideous, knobby, reddish hands, with nails cut straight and not always too clean; but once when in one of those magazines his eye fell on a photograph of an archaic Greek statue, the sort with wide-set eyes and an ambiguous smile, I was surprised to see his splayed finger tips stroke the picture with a delicacy that was almost regal. He noticed I was watching him, gave a grunt of fury, and ordered another coffee.

But for a lucky accident our relations would have remained on this plane of latent hostility. I used to bring over five or six newspapers from the office, among them, once, the *Giornale di Sicilia*. Those were the years when the Ministry of so-called Popular Culture was at its fiercest, and all newspapers were identical; that number of the Palermo daily was more banal than ever and only distinguishable from a paper of Rome or Milan by its bad typography; so my reading of it was brief, and I soon dropped the sheet on the table. I had just begun to contemplate yet another incarnation of "Minculpop," when I was addressed by my neighbor: "Excuse me, sir, but might I glance at this *Giornale di Sicilia* of yours? I'm Sicilian and it's twenty years since I've seen a newspaper from home." The voice was cultivated, its accent impeccable; the old man's gray eyes looked at me with utter detachment. "Please do, of course. You know I'm Sicilian too, and if you wish I could easily bring you the newspaper here every evening." "Thank you, I don't think that's necessary; my curiosity is purely physical. If Sicily is still as it was in my day, I imagine nothing good ever happens there as it hasn't for three thousand years."

He took a listless glance over the newspaper, refolded it, handed it back to me, and plunged into reading a pamphlet. When leaving he obviously wanted to slip off without a greeting, but I got up and introduced myself; he muttered through his teeth a name which I could not catch, but did not hold out his hand. On the threshold of the café, however, he turned around, raised his hat, and called out, "Hail, fellow countryman!" Then he vanished beneath the arcades, leaving me dumbfounded and provoking moans of disapproval among the gambling ghosts.

I wove suitable magic spells to materialize a waiter and asked him, pointing to the empty table, "Who was that gentleman?" "That," he replied, "is Senator Rosario La Ciura."

The name meant a lot even to my patchy journalist's culture: it was that of one of the five or six Italians who possess a reputation universal and unassailable, that of the most illustrious Hellenist of our time. Now I understood the bulky reviews and the stroking of that print; the irritability too, and the hidden refinement.

Next day at the office I searched around in that odd card index of obituaries still "in suspense." There was a card for "La Ciura" there, decently filled in for once. It said how the great man was born at Aci-Castello (Catania) from a lower-middle-class family and, through his amazing aptitude for studying Greek, had by dint of scholarships and erudite publications attained the Chair of Greek Literature at the University of Pavia at the age of twenty-seven; he had then been called to the Chair at Turin, where he had stayed until reaching the age limit; he had lectured at Oxford and Tübingen, and traveled extensively, for he was not only a pre-Fascist senator and Academician of the Lincei, but also doctor *honoris causa* of Yale, Harvard, New Delhi, and Tokyo, as well, of course, as of the most illustrious universities in Europe from Upsala to Salamanca. The list of his publications was very lengthy, and many of his works, particularly on Ionic dialects, were considered basic; proof of this was the fact that, though a foreigner, he had been charged with the Teubner edition of Hesiod, for which he had written an introduction, in Latin, of unrivaled mastery; final, major glory, he was *not* a member of the Italian Academy. What had always distinguished him from colleagues, however erudite, was his lively, almost carnal sense of classical antiquity; and this was shown in a collection of essays in Italian, *Men and Gods,* which was considered a work not only of high erudition but of true poetry. In fact, concluded the compiler of the card, he was "an honor to a nation and a beacon to all cultures." He was seventy-five years old, and lived, not opulently but decently enough, on his pension and his senatorial emolument. He was unmarried.

There's no denying it: we Italians, elder sons (or fathers) of the Renaissance, consider the Great Humanist to be the highest form of human being. The chance of now finding myself in daily contact with the highest representative of this subtle, almost magical, and unremunerative branch of knowledge, flattered and perturbed me; I felt the same sensations as a young American might feel on introduction to Mr. Gillette: alarm, respect, and a form of not ignoble envy.

That evening I went down to Limbo in a very different mood from that of the days before. The Senator was already in his place and answered my reverential greeting with a scarcely perceptible mumble. But when he had finished reading an article and completing some notes on a little pad, he turned toward me and in strangely musical

tones said, "Fellow countryman, from your way of greeting me I see that one of these phantoms must have told
you who I am. Forget it and, if you have not done so
already, forget also the aorists you studied at school. But
tell me what your name is, for last night you made the
usual gabbled introduction and I cannot fall back, like
you, on asking others for your name, which is certainly
quite unknown to anyone here."

He was talking with insolent detachment; obviously
to him I was rather less than a cockroach, more like one
of those specks of dust that rotate unconstructively in
sunbeams. But his calm tone, his precise speech, his use
of the familiar *"tu,"* radiated the serenity of a Platonic
dialogue.

"My name is Paolo Corbèra, and I was born at Palermo,
where I took a degree in law; now I am working here
in the editorial offices of *La Stampa.* To reassure you,
Senator, I will add that in my school-leaving exam I
only got five plus for Greek and have reason to think the
plus was added so that I could be given a certificate at all."

He gave a half-smile. "Thank you for telling me that;
better so. I detest talking to people who think themselves
knowledgeable when they are ignorant, like my colleagues

at the University; really all they know are the exterior forms of Greek, its oddities and deformities. The live spirit of that language which is so stupidly called "dead" has not been revealed to them. Nothing has been revealed to them, if it comes to that. Poor wretches, anyway; how can they sense that spirit if they have never had occasion to hear real Greek?"

Pride is preferable to false modesty, yes indeed; but I felt the Senator was rather overdoing it; it even occurred to me that the years might have softened that exceptional brain a bit. Those poor devils his colleagues had just the same chance of hearing ancient Greek as he had himself: none at all, that is.

He was proceeding, "Paolo . . . You are lucky to be called after the only apostle with some culture and a smattering of letters. Jerome would have been better though. The other names you Christians carry around are really too squalid. Slaves' names."

I was feeling more and more disappointed; he seemed to be merely an ordinary academic priest-baiter with a dash of Nietzscheian Fascism added. Surely not?

He was talking on with the seductive modulations and

the verve of a man who had perhaps spent a long time in silence. "Corbèra . . . Am I mistaken in thinking that to be one of the great Sicilian names? I remember my father used to pay a small annual ground rent for our house at Aci-Castello to the agent of a family called Corbèra di Palina or Salina, I don't remember which. He used to make a joke every time, in fact, and say that if there was any sure thing in this world it was that those few lire would not end in the pockets of the 'demesne,' as he called them. But are you really one of those Corbèras or merely a descendant of some peasant who took his master's name?"

I confessed myself to be indeed a Corbèra di Salina, in fact the only surviving specimen of that family; all the splendors, all the sins, all the unexacted rents, all the unpaid bills, all the Leopard's ways in fact, were concentrated in me alone. Paradoxically the Senator seemed pleased.

"Good, good. I hold old families in high regard. They possess a memory, minute it's true, but anyway greater than that of others. They are the best you people can achieve in the way of physical immortality. See you marry soon, Corbèra, since you people have found no better way of survival than dispersing your seed in the unlikeliest places."

Definitely, I was losing patience. "You people, you people." Who were "You people"? All the vile mob who had not the luck to be Senator La Ciura? Had *he* attained physical immortality? One wouldn't say so to look at that wrinkled face, that heavy body . . .

"Corbèra di Salina," he was continuing undaunted. "You won't be offended if I go on calling you '*tu*' as to one of those little students of mine during their few instants of youth?"

I declared myself not only honored but pleased, as in fact I was. Having disposed of matters of name and protocol, we talked of Sicily. He had not set foot on the island for twenty years, and the last time he was "down there" (as he said in the Piedmontese manner) he had only stayed five days, at Syracuse, to discuss with Paolo Orsi* certain matters concerning the alteration of semichoruses in classic drama. "I remember they wanted to take me by motorcar from Catania to Syracuse; I only accepted on learning that at Augusta the road runs far from the sea,

* A former director of the Syracuse Museum.

while the railroad is along the shore. Tell me about that island of ours; it is a lovely land though inhabited by donkeys. The Gods have sojourned there, may still do so in inexorable Augusts. Let us not, though, mention those four modern temples; anyway, you know nothing about them, that I'm sure."

So we spoke about eternal Sicily, nature's Sicily; about the scent of rosemary on the Nèbrodi hills, the taste of Melilli honey, the waving grain seen from Enna on a windy day in May, the solitudes around Syracuse, the gusts of scent from orange and lemon gardens pouring over Palermo, it's said, during some sunsets in June. We talked of the enchantment of certain summer nights within sight of Castellamare Bay, when stars are mirrored in the sleeping sea and the spirit of anyone lying back among the lentisks is lost in a vortex of sky, while the body is tense and alert, fearing the approach of demons.

After an almost total absence of fifty years the Senator still kept an extraordinarily clear memory of a few little facts. "The sea! The sea of Sicily is the most colored, the most romantic of all I have ever seen. That will be the only thing you will not manage to ruin, apart from the cities, of course. In taverns by the sea do they still serve those prickly sea urchins split in half?" I reassured him, though adding that few ate them nowadays for fear of typhus. "Yet they're the best thing you have down there, those blood-red cartilages, those images of female organs, tasting of salt and seaweed. Typhus indeed! They're dangerous as are all gifts of the sea, which grant death together with immortality. At Syracuse I absolutely demanded some from Orsi. What flavor! What divine aspect! My finest memory in the last fifty years!"

I was confused and fascinated; a man like this abandoning himself to almost obscene metaphors, showing a childish greed for the, after all, mediocre delights of sea urchins!

We went on talking for a long time, and on leaving he insisted on paying for my coffee, not without an exhibition of his peculiar boorishness ("Of course, these lads of good family never have a cent in their pockets!"); and we parted friends, if one leaves out of account the fifty years dividing our ages and the thousands of light-years separating our cultures.

We went on meeting every evening, and although the smoke of my rage against humanity was now beginning to disperse I still made a point of meeting the Senator unfailingly in the infernal regions of Via Po. Not that we chatted much: he would go on reading and taking notes and only addressed me now and again, but when he did it was always a harmonious flow of pride and insolence, sprinkled with varied allusions, veined with incomprehensible poetry.

He went on spitting, too, and eventually I noticed that he did so only while reading. I think he must have acquired a certain affection for me too, but I am under no illusions about that; if he did have any, it was not what one of "us people" (to use the Senator's term) might feel for a human being, but more like an old spinster's affection for her pet canary, of whose fatuity and incomprehension she is aware but whose existence permits her to express aloud regrets in which the little creature has no part; on the other hand, if it were not there, she would feel ill at ease. I began noticing, in fact, that whenever I was late the old man's haughty eyes were fixed on the entrance door.

It took nearly a month for us to move on from his always highly original but general comments to the indiscretions which alone make conversations between friends differ from those between mere acquaintances. I myself took the initiative. That frequent spitting of his worried me (as it worried the custodians of the Hades, who had eventually put a dark copper spittoon beside his chair), and one evening I was bold enough to ask him why he did not go to a doctor about his chronic catarrh. I asked the question unthinkingly, at once regretted having risked it, and waited for the senatorial anger to bring the stucco ceiling down on my head. Instead of which the well-modulated voice replied placidly, "But, my dear Corbèra, I have no catarrh. A keen observer like yourself should have noticed that I never cough before I spit. My spitting is no sign of illness, but rather of mental health. I spit from disgust at the nonsense I am reading. If you care to examine that utensil there" (and he pointed at the spittoon) "you will realize that it contains very little saliva and no trace of mucus. My spits are symbolic and of high cultural content; if you don't like 'em then go back to your native drawing rooms where there's no spitting only because no one will ever admit themselves to be nauseated by anything."

The gross insolence of this was attenuated by a faraway look, yet even so I felt like getting up and leaving him there and then; luckily I had time to reflect that I had only my own rashness to blame. I stayed, and at once the impassive Senator counterattacked: "Now *you* tell *me* why you frequent this ghost-filled and, as you say, catarrh-ridden Erebus, this geometric site of failed lives. In Turin there's no lack of those creatures who to you people seem so desirable. A trip to that hotel by the castle, to Rivoli or the baths at Moncalieri, and your prurient pastime would soon find an object." I burst into laughter at hearing from so learned a mouth such exact information on the pleasure haunts of Turin. "But how d'you come to know these addresses, Senator?" "I know them, Corbèra, I know them. That is the one thing, and the one thing only, that one does learn from frequenting Senates, both academic and political. But please do me the favor of being convinced that the sordid pleasures of you people have never been for Rosario La Ciura." That, one felt, was true: the Senator's bearing and words bore the unequivocal sign (as we used to say in 1938) of a sexual reserve quite unconnected with age.

"The truth, Senator, is that I began coming here as a temporary refuge from the world. I've had trouble with two of the sort of girls so justly stigmatized by you."

His reply was sharp and frank. "Cuckoldry, eh, Cor-bèra? Or disease?"

"Neither: worse: desertion." And I told him about the ridiculous events of two months before. My tone was facetious, for the ulcer on my self-respect had healed up. Any man other than this devilish Hellenist would have either jeered at me or, more rarely, sympathized. But the alarming old man did neither: he waxed indignant. "You see what happens, Corbèra, as a result of coupling with the squalid and the diseased? I would say the same to those two sluts about you, if I ever had the misfortune to meet them."

"Diseased, Senator? They were both in superb health; you should have seen the amount they ate at the *Specchi;* and not in the least squalid: splendid creatures, both of them, and elegant too." The Senator hissed out one of his contemptuous spits. "Diseased, I said, diseased: they'll crack up in fifty, sixty years, maybe long before; so from now on they're sick. And squalid: elegant indeed, with their trashy jewelry, stolen pullovers, and airs and graces taken from the films! Splendor indeed, fishing about for greasy bank notes in their lover's pocket instead of pre-senting him, as do others, with rose-pink pearls and coral branches. That's just what happens when people go with these tawdry sluts. And were you not at all disgusted, they as much as you, you as much as they, at cuddling future carcasses between stinking sheets?" I was stupid enough to reply, "But the sheets were always perfectly clean, Senator!" He became furious. "What have sheets to do with it? The inevitable stink of corpses was your own. I repeat, how can you all wallow about with people of their, of your sort?" I, who had just been eying one of Ventura's delicious *cousettes,* took offense. "Well, one can't go to bed only with Serene Highnesses!" "Who mentioned 'Serene Highnesses'? They're as much charnel-house material as the others. But these are matters you cannot understand, young man, and I am wrong to mention them. You and your little girl friends are fated to sink deeper and deeper into the pestilential mire of your dirty pleasures. Those who really know are so few."

He began to smile with eyes turned toward the ceiling; his face had a rapt expression; then he held out his hand to me and left.

He did not appear again for three days; on the fourth I had a telephone call at the newspaper office. "Is that

Monsù Corbèra? This is Bettina, housekeeper to *Signour* Senator La Ciura. He says to tell you that he's had a bad cold, that he's better now, and that he'd like to see you tonight after dinner. Come to 18, Via Bertola at nine; second floor." The line was suddenly cut, and I could not ring back.

Number 18 Via Bertola was a dilapidated old building, but the Senator's apartment was large and well kept, due, presumably, to the insistent care of Bettina. The parade of books began from the entrance hall, the sort of modest-looking cheaply bound volumes of every living library. There were thousands in the three rooms I crossed. In the fourth sat the Senator wrapped in an ample camel's hair dressing gown, the finest and softest I had ever seen. Later I learned this was not camel's-hair but rare llama wool, a gift from the Academic Senate of Lima. Though the Senator pointedly did not rise on my entry, he greeted me most cordially; he felt better, quite well in fact, and expected to be back in circulation as soon as the wave of cold then over Turin grew milder. He offered me some resinated Cypriot wine, a gift from the Italian Institute of Athens, some ghastly pink loukoums from the Archae-ological Mission of Ankara, and sensible Torinese cakes

acquired by the provident Bettina. He was in such good
humor that he actually smiled twice with his whole
mouth and even reached the point of apologizing for his
own outbursts in our Hades. "I know, Corbèra, I have
been excessive in my terms, though believe me, moderate
in my concepts. Don't give it another thought." I was in
fact not thinking of it, but feeling full of respect for this
old man whom I suspected of being very unhappy in spite
of his triumphant career. He was devouring those abomi-
nable loukoums. "Sweets, Corbèra, should be sweet and
no more. If they have any other flavor they're like perverse
kisses."

He was giving big morsels to Aeacus, a large boxer
dog which had entered the room. "This creature, Corbèra,
in spite of his ugliness, is more like the Immortals, to
one who can understand such things, than are your little
bitches."

He refused to show me his library. "All classics that
could have no interest for one like you, morally failed in
Greek." But he did take me around the room we were
in, which turned out to be his study. It contained few
books, among them the plays of Tirso de Molina, La
Motte Fouqué's *L'Undine*, Giraudoux's play of the same

name, and, to my surprise, the works of H. G. Wells. But in compensation the walls were hung with huge photographs, life-size, of archaic Greek statues; and not the usual photographs we can all lay hands on, but superb specimens, obviously demanded with authority and dispatched with devotion from museums all over the world. There they all were, those magnificent creatures: the "Rider" in the Louvre, the "Seated Goddess" from Taranto now in Berlin, the "Warrior" of Delphi, the "Korè" of the Acropolis, the "Apollo" of Piombino, the "Lapithae Woman" and the "Phœbus" at Olympia, the famous "Charioteer" . . . The room was alight with their ecstatic yet ironic smiles, exalted by the relaxed arrogance of their bearing. "You see, Corbèra: these yes; little tarts no."

On the mantelpiece were ancient amphoræ and vases: Odysseus tied to the ship's mast, the Sirens crashing from a high precipice onto rocks in expiation for letting their prey escape. "All nonsense that, Corbèra, petty bourgeois poets' tales. None ever escapes the Sirens, and even if someone did they would never have died for so little. How could they have died, anyway?"

On a small table, in a modest frame, stood an old faded

photograph: a youth of about twenty, almost naked, with unruly curls and a confident look on features of rare beauty. Perplexed, I paused an instant, thinking I'd understood. Not at all. "And this, fellow countryman, this was and is and shall be" (he accentuated strongly) "Rosario La Ciura."

· The poor senator in a dressing gown had been a young god.

Then we spoke of other things, and before I left he showed me a letter in French from the Rector of the University of Coimbra inviting him to join the Committee of Honor for a congress of Greek studies which was to take place in Portugal that May. "I'm very pleased about it; I'll embark at Genoa on the *Rex* with the French, Swiss, and German congress members. Like Odysseus I shall stop my ears to avoid hearing the nonsense of those maimed creatures; there will be lovely days of navigation: sun, blue, smell of sea."

On our way out we passed the bookcase holding the works of Wells, and I dared to express my surprise at finding them there. "You're right, Corbèra, they're a horror. And among them there's a short novel that would make me want to spit for a month on end if I reread it; and you wouldn't like that, would you, you drawing-room lapdog?"

After this visit of mine our relations became definitely cordial, on my side at least. I made elaborate preparations for some really fresh sea urchins to be sent up from Genoa. When told they would arrive next day I laid in some Etna wine and peasant bread, then timidly invited the Senator to visit my little abode. I went to fetch him in my Fiat *Balilla,* and drove him all the way out to Via Peyron, which is at the back of beyond. In the car he showed some alarm and utter distrust in my driving capacities. "I know you now, Corbèra; if we have the misfortune to meet one of those skirted monstrosities of yours you're quite capable of turning right around, then we'll both go and crack our noses on a curb." We met no noteworthy abortions in skirts and arrived intact.

For the first time since I had known him I saw the Senator laugh; this was on entering my bedroom. "So this is the theater of your grubby ruttings, is it, Corbèra!" He examined my few books. "Good, good. Maybe you're less ignorant than you seem. This man here," he added, taking up my Shakespeare, "this man here did understand something. *'A sea change into something rich and strange.' 'What potions have I drunk of Siren tears?'*"

When good Signora Carmagnola entered the sitting room with a tray of sea urchins, lemons, and the rest, the Senator was in ecstasies. "What? You thought of this, did you? How can you know that these are what I yearn for most?"

"You're quite safe in eating them, Senator, they were in the sea on the Riviera only this morning."

"Yes, of course, always the same, you people, slaves to decay and putrescence, always with ears strained for the shuffling steps of Death. Poor devils! Thank you, Corbèra, you've been a good *famulus*. A pity they're not from that sea 'down there,' these sea urchins, that they aren't wrapped in our own seaweed; their prickles have certainly never made any divine blood flow. You've done all you possibly could, of course, but these are almost wild sea urchins that were dozing in the chilly rocks of Nervi or Arenzano." Obviously he was one of those Sicilians who consider the Ligurian Riviera (a tropical region to the Milanese) a kind of Iceland. The sea urchins, split, exhibited their wounded, blood-red, strangely partitioned flesh. I had never noticed before, but now, after the Senator's bizarre comparisons, they really did seem to me like a cross section of some delicate female organ. He was eating them avidly but without gaiety, quiet, almost absorbed. He would squeeze no lemon over them. "You people are always coupling flavors! A sea urchin must taste of lemon too, sugar of chocolate, love of paradise!"

When he had finished he took a sip of wine, closed his eyes. Soon after, I noticed two tears slide from under his withered lids. He got up, moved over to the window, surreptitiously wiped his eyes. Then he turned. "Have you ever been to Augusta, Corbèra?"

I had been there three months as a recruit; during time off two or three of us used to take out a boat and meander around the transparent waters of the bays. After my reply he was silent; then he said in a tone of irritation, "And did you milksops ever visit that little inner bay beyond Punta Izzo, behind the hill overlooking the salt pans?"

"Indeed we did; it's the loveliest spot in Sicily, fortunately so far undiscovered by the Young Fascists' organizations. A wild bit of coast, isn't it, Senator? Utterly deserted, not a house in sight; the sea is peacock-colored; and right opposite, beyond the iridescent waves,

Etna. From nowhere else as from there is it so lovely, so calm, masterful, truly divine. It is one of those places in which one sees an eternal aspect of that island of ours which so idiotically turned its back on its vocation, that of serving as pasturage for the herds of the sun."

The Senator was silent. Then: "You're a good lad, Corbèra; if you were not so ignorant one could have made something of you."

He came up to me, kissed me on the forehead. "Now go and fetch that little coffee grinder of yours. I want to go home."

During the following weeks we went on meeting as usual. Now we would take nocturnal walks, usually along Via Po and across the martial Piazza Vittorio in order to gaze at the rushing river and the Hill, where they introduced a touch of fantasy into the geometric pattern of the city. It was the beginning of spring, that touching season of threatened youth; first lilacs were sprouting on banks, the more eager havenless couples already defying damp grass. "Down in Sicily the sun is already burning, the seaweed aflower; fish are surfacing on moonlight nights, their flashing bodies are glimpsed amid luminous spray. And here we stand facing this insipid and deserted stream, these great barracks that look like rows of soldiers or friars, and hear the moaning of these couplings of the dying."

But he cheered at the thought of the sea journey he would soon be taking to Lisbon; departure was close now. "It will be pleasant; you should come too; a pity, though, that there's no group for people deficient in Greek; you could talk Italian to me, but if you didn't show Zuckmayer or Van der Voos a knowledge of the optatives of all irregular Greek verbs you'd be done for. Maybe, though, you are more conscious of Greek reality than they; not by culture, of course, but by animal instincts."

Two days before he left for Genoa he told me he would not be coming to the café next day but be expecting me at his home at nine that night.

The ceremonial was the same as on my other visit: the pictures of the gods of three thousand years ago radiated youth as a stove radiates heat; the faded photograph of the young god of fifty years before seemed dismayed to look at his own metamorphosis, white-haired and slumped in an armchair.

When the Cypriot wine was drunk the Senator called

for Bettina and told her she could go to bed. "I will see Signor Corbèra out myself when he goes. Now, Corbèra, if I've brought you here tonight at the risk of disarranging one of your fornications at Rivoli, it's because I need you. I leave tomorrow, and when one goes away at my age one never knows if it won't be a matter of staying afar forever; particularly on a journey by sea. You know, really, I'm quite fond of you; your simplicity touches me, the obvious machinations of your vital forces amuse me; then I have an idea that you, as happens with a few Sicilians of the better kind, have succeeded in achieving a synthesis between your senses and your reason. So you deserve not to be left dry-mouthed, without my explaining to you the reason for some of my oddities, for some of the phrases I have uttered in front of you and which you must have thought worthy of a madman."

I protested feebly, "Much of what you said I've not understood; but I've always attributed my incomprehension to the inadequacy of my own mind, never to an aberration of yours."

"No matter, Corbèra, it's all the same to me. All us old men seem mad to you young ones, yet often it's the other way around. To explain myself, though, I shall have to describe my adventure to you, which is unusual. It happened when I was that young gentleman there," and he pointed to the photograph of himself. "We must go back to 1887, a time which must seem prehistoric to you, but is not so to me."

He moved from his own chair behind the desk and came to sit on the sofa beside me. "Excuse me, you know, but later on I'll have to speak in a low voice. Important words can't be yelled; the scream of love or hate is only heard in melodramas or among the most uncivilized, which comes to the same thing. Anyway, in 1887 I was twenty-four years old; my aspect was that of the photograph; I already had a degree in classics, and had published two small studies on Ionic dialects which had made some stir at my university; and for the last year I'd been preparing to compete for a chair at Pavia University. To say the truth, never, before that year or since, had I or have I touched a woman."

I was sure that my face remained marmoreally impassive, but I was deceived. "That wink of yours is very ill-mannered, Corbèra. What I'm saying is the truth; truth and also boast. I know that we males of Catania are generally thought capable of making our very wet-nurses pregnant, which may well be true. Not in my case, though. When one spends night and day in the company of gods and demigods, as I was doing at the time, one is left with little desire to climb the stairs of San Berillio brothels. Also I was held back by religious scruples at the time. Corbèra, you really must learn to control your eyelashes: they betray you again and again. Yes. Religious scruples, I said. I also said 'at the time.' Now I no longer have them, but that's been no use to me in this matter.

"You, my little Corbèra, who probably got your job on the newspaper owing to a note from some Fascist boss, can have no idea of the preparation needed to compete for a university chair in Greek literature. It means two years of slogging away to the verge of madness. The language, luckily, I knew well enough already, as well as I do now; and I don't wish to boast, but . . . It was the rest: the Alexandrian and Byzantine variants of texts, the quotations, always inaccurate, perpetrated by Latin authors, the innumerable connections between literature and mythology, history, philosophy, science! I repeat, it's enough to drive anyone mad. So there I was studying away and, on top of that, cramming boys who'd failed their school exams, in order to pay my keep in town. I was living on more or less nothing but black olives and coffee. Then to crown it all came that appalling summer of 1887, which was one of the truly hellish ones that happen down there now and again. At night Etna would vomit the sun's fire that it had stored during fifteen hours of daylight; touching a balcony rail at midday meant a rush to a First Aid post; the lava paving stones seemed on the point of returning to their fluid state; and almost every day the sirocco flapped its slimy bats' wings in one's face. I was all in. A friend saved me: he met me as I was wandering deranged through the streets, stuttering Greek verses which I no longer understood. My appearance alarmed him. 'Listen, Rosario, if you stay on here you'll go off your head and that will be the end of your chair. I'm off to Switzerland' (the boy had money) 'but I've a three-room hut at Augusta twenty yards from the sea, way out of town. Pack your bag, take your books, and go and spend the whole summer there. Call at my home in an hour's time and I'll give you the key. You'll see, it's quite different there. Ask at the station where the Casino Carobene is, everyone knows it. But do leave, leave tonight.'

"I took his advice and left that night; next morning, instead of being greeted at dawn by sewer pipes across a courtyard, I woke up facing a pure stretch of sea with, in the background, an Etna no longer ruthless, wrapped in morning mist. The port was utterly deserted, as you tell me it still is, and uniquely lovely. All that the shabby rooms of the little house contained were the couch on which I spent the night, a table, and three chairs; also a few earthenware pots and an old lamp in the kitchen. Behind the house was a fig tree and a well. Paradise. I went into town, traced the peasant who looked after Carobene's patch of land, and arranged for him to bring me bread, spaghetti, a few vegetables, and some kerosene every two or three days. Oil I had, our own, sent by my poor mother down to Catania. I hired a small boat which a fisherman brought me over every afternoon together with a lobster pot and a few fishing hooks. There I made up my mind to stay at least two months.

"Carobene was right: it really was quite different. The heat was violent at Augusta too, but it no longer reverberated from every wall, no longer produced utter prostration but a kind of suppressed euphoria; the sun put off its executioner's scowl and contented itself with the role of splendid if brutal donor of energy, as well as of a magic jeweler who set mobile diamonds in every slightest ripple of sea. Study had ceased to be an effort; to the gentle rocking of the boat in which I spent long hours each book became, instead of an obstacle, a key opening up a world one of whose most entrancing aspects I already had beneath my eyes. Often I found myself declaiming verses of poets aloud, and the names of those forgotten gods, ignored by most, again skimmed the surface of that sea which once at their name alone had risen in tumult or relapsed into a lull.

"My isolation was complete, interrupted only by visits from the peasant who brought me a few provisions every three or four days. He only stayed five minutes because the sight of my elated carefree state must have made him think me on the verge of dangerous madness. And, in truth, sun, solitude, nights spent beneath rotating stars, silence, sparse feeding, study of remote subjects, did weave a kind of spell around me which predisposed a mood for prodigy.

"This was fulfilled at six o'clock on the morning of the fifth of August. I had just awakened and got straight into the boat; a few strokes of the oars had borne me far from the pebbles on the beach and I had stopped under a large rock whose shadow would protect me from the sun, already climbing in swollen ferment and changing to gold and blue the candor of the dawn sea. I was declaiming away when I suddenly felt the edge of the boat lower, to the right, behind me, as if someone had seized it to climb on board. I turned and saw her: a smooth sixteen-year-old face emerging from the sea, two small hands gripping the gunwale. The girl smiled, a slight fold drawing aside her pale lips and showing a glimpse of sharp little white teeth like a dog's. But it was not in the least like one of those smiles you people give, which are always debased by an accessory expression, of benevolence or irony, pity, cruelty, or the like; this expressed nothing but itself, that is an almost animal joy, an almost divine delight in existence. This smile was the first of the spells cast upon me, revealing paradises of forgotten serenity. From rumpled sun-colored hair the sea water flowed over green, very wide-open eyes down features of childlike purity.

"Our captious reason, however predisposed, rears up before a prodigy, and when faced with one falls back on memories of the obvious; I tried, as anyone else would, to persuade myself I had met a girl out bathing, and moved carefully over above her, bent down, and held out my hands to help her in. But she, with astounding vigor, emerged straight from the sea as far as the waist and put her arms around my neck, enveloping me in a scent I had never smelled before, then let herself slither into the boat: beneath her groin, beneath her gluteal muscles, her body was that of a fish, covered in minute scales of blue and mother-of-pearl, and ending in a forked tail which was slowly beating the bottom of the boat. She was a mermaid.

"She lay on her back with head resting on crossed hands, showing with serene immodesty a delicate down under her armpits, drawn-apart breasts, perfectly shaped loins; from her arose what I have wrongly called a scent but was more a magic smell of sea, of youthful voluptuousness. We were in shade, but twenty yards away the beach lay abandoned to the sun and quivering with pleasure. My reaction was ill hidden by my almost complete nudity.

"She spoke: and so after her smile and her smell I was submerged by the third and greatest of charms, that of voice. It was slightly guttural, veiled, reverberating with innumerable harmonies; behind the words could be sensed the lazy surf of summer seas, last spray rustling on a beach, winds passing on lunar waves. The song of the

Sirens does not exist, Corbèra: the music from which there is no escaping is that of their voices.

"She was speaking in Greek and I had great trouble in understanding her: 'I heard you talking to yourself in a language similar to my own; I like you, take me. I am Lighea, daughter of Calliope. Do not believe in the tales invented about us; we kill none, we only love.'

"Bent over her, I rowed, staring into her laughing eyes. We reached the shore; I took that aromatic body in my arms and we passed from glare to deep shade; she was already bringing to my mouth that flavor of pleasure which compared to your earthly kisses is like wine to tap water."

The Senator was describing his adventure in a low voice. I, who in my heart had always considered my own varied sexual experiences far superior to what I had thought of as his mediocre ones, and who had stupidly felt that this diminished the distance between us, was humiliated; even in love I found myself submerged in abysmal depths below him. Never for an instant did I suspect him to be telling me lies, and the greatest skeptic, had he been present, would have sensed the utter truth in the old man's tone.

"So those three weeks began. It is not proper, it would anyway not be charitable toward you, to enter into details. Suffice it to say that in those embraces I enjoyed both the highest forms of spiritual pleasure and that elementary one, quite without any social connotations, felt by our lonely shepherds on the hills when they couple with their own goats; if the comparison disgusts you that is because you are incapable of making the necessary transposition from the bestial to the superhuman planes, in my case superimposed on each other.

"Think again of what Balzac dared not express in his 'Une Passion dans le désert.' Those immortal limbs of hers emanated such a life force that every loss of energy was at once replenished, in fact increased. During those days, Corbèra, I loved as much as a hundred of your Don Juans put together in their whole lives. And what love! Immune from convents or crimes, from Commander's rages and Leporello's trivialities, away from the pretensions of the heart, from the false sighs and sham deliquescence which inevitably blot your wretched kisses. A Leporello did, actually, disturb us that first day; it was the only time: toward ten o'clock I heard the peasant's heavy boots on the path leading to the sea. Scarcely had

I time to draw a sheet over Lighea's unusual figure when he was already at the door: her head, neck, and arms, which were uncovered, made Leporello think it was some ordinary little romp and this induced a sudden respect in him; he stayed for even less time than usual and as he went off winked his left eye and with thumb and forefinger of his right hand rolled and shut, he made a gesture of twiddling an imaginary mustache at the corner of his mouth; then he clambered off up the path.

"I have spoken of our spending twenty days together; but I would not like you to think that during those three weeks she and I lived as 'man and wife,' as the expression goes, sharing bed, food, and occupations. Lighea was very often away; without any previous hint she would plunge into the sea and vanish, sometimes for many hours. When she returned, usually early in the morning, she would either meet me in the boat, or, if I was still indoors, slither on her back over the pebbles, half in and half out of the water, pushing herself along by the arms and calling for me to help her up the slope. 'Sasà,' she used to call me, as I had told her that was the diminutive of my name. In this action, hampered by that very part of her body which made her so agile in the sea, she had the pitiful aspect of a wounded animal, an aspect which the laughter in her eyes canceled at once.

"She ate only what was alive: often I saw her emerge from the sea, her delicate torso gleaming in the sun, and tearing in her teeth a silvery fish that was still quivering; the blood flowed in lines down her chin, and after a few bites the mangled codfish or dory would be flung over her shoulder and sink into the water, tainting it with red, while she let out childish cries as she cleaned her teeth with her tongue. Once I gave her some wine; she was incapable of drinking from a glass, and I had to pour some into her minute and faintly greenish palm, from which she drank by lapping it up with her tongue like a dog, while surprise spread in her eyes at that unknown flavor. She said it was good, but always refused it afterward. Occasionally she would come ashore with hands full of oysters and mussels, and while I labored to open the shells with a knife she would crack them with a stone and suck in the palpitating mollusk together with shreds of shell which did not bother her.

"As I told you, Corbèra, she was a beast but at the same instant also an Immortal, and it is a pity that no speech

can express this synthesis continually, with such utter simplicity, as she expressed it in her own body. Not only did
she show a joyousness and delicacy in the carnal act quite
the opposite of dreary animal lust, but her talk had a
potent immediacy which I have found since only in a few
great poets. Not for nothing is she the daughter of
Calliope: ignorant of all culture, unaware of all wisdom,
contemptuous of any moral inhibitions, she belonged,
even so, to the fountainhead of all culture, of all wisdom,
of all ethics, and could express this primigenial superiority
of hers in terms of rugged beauty. 'I am everything because
I am simply the current of life, with its detail eliminated; I
am immortal because in me every death meets, from that
of the fish just now to that of Zeus, and conjoined in me
they turn again into a life that is no longer individual and
determined but of Pan and so free.' Then she would say,
'You are young and handsome; follow me now into the
sea and you will avoid sorrow and old age; come to my
dwelling beneath the high mountains of dark motionless
waters where all is silence and quiet, so infused that who
possesses it does not even notice it. I have loved you; and
remember that when you are tired, when you can drag on

no longer, you have only to lean over the sea and call me; I will always be there, because I am everywhere, and your thirst for sleep will be assuaged.'

"She told me about her existence beneath the sea, about bearded Tritons and translucent caverns, but she said that those too were unreal visions and that the truth lay much deeper, in the blind mute palace of formless waters, eternal, without a gleam, without a whisper.

"Once she told me she would be away a long while, till the evening of the next day. 'I must go a long way off, to where I know I shall find a gift for you.'

"She returned with a superb branch of lilac coral encrusted with sea shells and barnacles. For years I used to keep this in a drawer and kiss every night the places where I remembered to have rested the fingers of the Indifferent, that is, of the Beneficent One. Then one day Maria, a housekeeper of mine before Bettina, stole it to give to a pimp. I found it later at a goldsmith's on the Ponte Vecchio, desecrated, cleaned and polished so that it was almost unrecognizable. I bought it back and that night flung it into the Arno: it had passed through too many hands.

"She also spoke of the considerable number of human

lovers she had had during that millennial adolescence of
hers: fishermen and sailors, Greek, Sicilian, Arab, Capresi;
one or two shipwrecked mariners too, adrift on rotting
rafts, to whom she had appeared for a second, in the lightning flashes of a storm, to change their death rattle into
ecstasy. 'All have followed up my invitation and come to
me again, some at once, others after the passage of what
for them was a long time. There was only one I never
saw again: a fine big lad with very white skin and red
hair with whom I coupled on a distant beach over where
our sea joins the great Ocean; he smelled of something
even stronger than that wine you gave me the other day.
I think he never appeared not because I did not make him
happy but because he was so drunk when we met that he
did not understand a thing; I probably seemed like one of
his usual fishergirls.'

"Those weeks of high summer sped by as fast as a
single morning; when they were over I realized that
actually I had lived for centuries. That lascivious girl,
that cruel wild beast, had also been a Wise Mother who,
by her mere presence, had uprooted faiths, dissipated
metaphysics. With those fragile, often blood-covered fingers, she had shown me the way toward true eternal

repose, and also toward an asceticism derived not from renunciation but from incapacity to accept other inferior pleasures. Certainly I shall not be the second man to disobey her call; I will not refuse that kind of pagan Grace that has been conceded me.

"Due to its very violence, that summer was short. Just after the twentieth of August, the first timid clouds began collecting, and a few isolated drops of rain fell, tepid as blood. The nights were an enfolding chain of slow, mute lightning flashes following each other on the distant horizon, like the cogitations of a god. In the mornings the dove-colored sea would moan like a turtledove with arcane restlessness, and in the evenings crinkle without any perceptible breeze in gradations of smoke-gray, steel-gray, pearl-gray, all gentle colors more tender than the former splendor. Far away wisps of mist grazed the waters: perhaps on the coasts of Greece it was already raining. Lighea's mood also changed in color from splendor to tender gray. She was silent more often, spent hours stretched on a rock gazing at a horizon no longer motionless, seldom went away. 'I want to stay on with you; if I leave the shore now my companions of the sea will keep me back. Do you hear them? They're calling me.' Some-

times I did seem to hear a different, lower note amid the
screech of sea gulls, to glimpse unruly flashes from rock
to rock. 'They are sounding their shells, calling Lighea
for the storm festival!'

"This hit us at dawn on the twenty-sixth. From the rock
we saw the wind sweep closer, flinging the distant waters
into confusion, as near us swelled vast and leaden billows.
Soon the broadside reached us, whistled in our ears, bent
the dried-up rosemary bushes. The sea below us did not
break; along came the first white-crowned wave. 'Good-
by, Sasà. You won't forget!' The roller crashed on our
rock, the mermaid flung herself into the iridescent surf; I
did not see her drop; she seemed to dissolve into the
spray."

The Senator left next morning; I went to the station to
see him off. He was grumpy and acid as always, but just
when the train began to move his fingers reached out of
the little window and grazed my head.

Next day, at dawn, came a telephone call to the newspaper from Genoa: during the night Senator La Ciura
had fallen into the sea from the deck of the *Rex* as it was
steaming toward Naples, and although lifeboats had

been launched at once the body had not been found.

A week later his will was opened: the money in the bank and his furniture went to Bettina; the library was left to the University of Catania; by a codicil of recent date I was left the Greek vase with the Siren figures and a large photograph of the Korè on the Acropolis.

Both objects I sent down to my home in Palermo. Then came the war and, while I was in Marmarica rationed to half a liter of water a day, "Liberators" destroyed my home; on my return I found the photograph had been cut into strips to serve as torches for night looters; the bowl was smashed; in the largest fragment can be seen the feet of Ulysses tied to his ship's mast. I still keep it. The books were stored in cellars at the University, but as there is no money for shelves they are slowly rotting away.

The Blind Kittens

THE FIRST CHAPTER OF AN UNCOMPLETED NOVEL

[*March, 1957*]

THE PLAN of the Ibba property, on a scale of 1 to 5,000, covered a strip of oiled paper six feet long and two and a half feet wide. Not that everything shown on the map belonged to the family: there was, first of all, to the south a narrow strip of sea belonging to no one on a coast line fringed with tunny fisheries; to the north were inhospitable mountains on which the Ibbas had never wanted to lay their hands; and amid the mass of lemon yellow indicating various family properties were a number of fair-sized white blobs: lands that never came on the market because the owners were rich; lands that had been offered but refused because they were of too low a quality; lands desired but in the hands of people who were still, as it were, undercooked, not yet fit for mastication. There were also a very few pieces of land which had been yellow and turned white again when resold to acquire other, better land during bad years when ready money was scarce. In spite of these splodges (all marginal), the main mass of yellow was imposing: from an oval-shaped inner nucleus around Gibilmonte a wide claw extended east-ward, gradually narrowed, then broadening again pushed out two tentacles, one toward the sea, which it reached for a small stretch, the other northward to the lower slopes of precipitous and sterile hills. Westward expansion was even bigger: these were ex-church lands in which advance had been as fast as a knife through lard: the hamlets of San Giacinto and San Narcisco had been oc-cupied and overrun by the flying columns of the Ex-propriation Acts; a defensive line on the river Favarotta had just collapsed after holding out a long time; and that day, the fourteenth of September, 1901, a bridgehead had been established on the far side of the river by the purchase of Pispisa, a small but succulent estate on the right bank.

The newly bought property had not yet been colored

in yellow on the plan, but Chinese ink and a thin brush
were already waiting on a desk for the hand of Calce-
donio, the only person in the house who knew how to
make proper use of them. Don Batassano Ibba himself,
head of the family and near-baron, had tried his hand
ten years before when Scíddico had been expropriated,
but with distressing results: a yellow tide had spread over
the whole map and a heap of money had to be spent on
having a new one done. The little bottle of ink, though,
was still the same. So this time Don Batassano did not
risk trying his hand, and merely stared with his brazen
peasant's eyes at the place to be colored, thinking that
the Ibba lands would show up now even on a map of all
Sicily, flea-size in the vastness of the island, of course,
but still clearly visible.

Don Batassano was satisfied but also irritated, two
states of mind often coexisting in him. That man Ferrara,
the Prince of Salina's agent who had arrived this morning to arrange the deed of sale, had quibbled right up to
the very moment of signature and even after! And he'd
wanted the money paid in eighty of the Bank of Sicily's
big pink notes instead of the letters of credit prepared
for him; he, Don Batassano, had had to climb upstairs and

draw the cash from a secret drawer in his own desk, a most risky operation because Mariannina and Totò might be around at that hour. True, the agent had let himself be bamboozled about a tithe of eighty lire a year to the Church Fund, for which he had agreed to take off a thousand six hundred lire from the capital value, while Don Batassano (and the notary too) knew that it had already been compounded nine years before by another of the Salina's agents. This had no effect though; any opposition, however slight, to his own will, particularly in regard to money, exasperated him: "They're forced to sell with the water up to their chins, but still fuss about the difference between bank notes and letters of credit!"

It was only four o'clock and there were five hours to go before supper. Don Batassano opened the window onto a narrow yard. The sultry September air, cooked, recooked, resteeped, infused the darkened room. Down below an old man with heavy mustaches was spreading birdlime on bamboo rods; he was preparing his young master's pastime. "Giacomino, saddle the horses, mine and yours. I'm coming down."

He wanted to go and see the damage to a water trough

at Scíddico: some urchins had smashed one side of a basin, so he had been told that morning; the leak had been stopped temporarily with rubble and that mixture of mud and straw always to be found beside horse troughs; but Tano, the tenant at Scíddico, had asked for proper repairs immediately. More bother, more expense; and if he did not go and see in person the workmen would put in an exorbitant bill. He assured himself that his holster with its heavy Smith & Wesson was hanging from his belt (he was so used to having it always on him that he no longer noticed it), and went down some slate steps into the yard. The keeper was just saddling the horses; he mounted his, from three brick steps put against a wall for that purpose, took a switch held out by a boy, waited until Giacomino (without help from his master's mounting steps) was in the saddle. The keeper's son flung open the fortified gates, summer afternoon light flooded the yard, and Don Batassano Ibba issued with his bodyguard into the main street of Gibilmonte.

The two rode along almost side by side, Giacomino's horse only half a head behind his master's; the keeper's "two-shooters" exhibited their iron butts, their polished barrels to right and left of the saddle. The animals' hoofs clattered irregularly over the cobbles of narrow alleys. Women sitting weaving in front of their doors gave no greeting. "Life!" cried Giacomino every now and again as some small completely naked urchin was about to roll between the horses' hoofs; dangling on a chair, his head against a wall of the church, the Archpriest pretended to be asleep: anyway the living was not in the gift of this rich Ibba here, but of the poor absentee Santapau. Only the sergeant of the *carabinieri,* in shirt sleeves at a balcony of the barracks, leaned over with a greeting. They left the village, climbed the track leading to the fork. A great deal of water had been lost during the night and it had formed a big stagnant pond all around: mixed with mud, chaff, manure, cows' urine, it exhaled a sharp stink of ammonia. But the temporary repairs had done their job; water was no longer flowing between cracks in the stone basin, only trickling, and the thin stream issuing in spurts from a rusty tube was enough to make up the loss. Don Batassano was so pleased that what had been done had cost nothing that he overlooked the repairs' temporary nature. "What nonsense Tano talked! The basin's in fine condition! It doesn't need a thing done to it. But tell the fool he must pull himself together and take care not to let my property be damaged by the first little brute who comes along. Tell 'im to find their fathers and have 'em talk to you if he doesn't do so himself."

On the way back a frightened rabbit crossed the track, Don Batassano's horse shied, kicked out, and the magnate, who had a fine little English saddle but insisted on twisted ropes instead of stirrups, ended on the ground. He was not hurt and Giacomino, well used to this situation, took the mare by the bridle and held it firm; from the ground Don Batassano whipped mercilessly up at the nose, ears, flanks of the animal, which was taken by a continuous quiver and beginning to foam. A kick in its belly ended the pedagogic operation, Don Batassano remounted, and the pair returned home just as it was growing dark.

Meanwhile Ferrara, unaware that the master of the house was out, had gone into the study, and finding it empty, sat down a moment to wait. The room contained a gun-rack with two rifles, a shelf with a few boxes ("Taxes," "Title deeds," "Cautions," "Mortgages" said the labels stuck on brown cardboard); on the desk was the deed of sale signed two hours before; behind, on the wall, that map.

The accountant got up to look closer: from his professional knowledge, from the innumerable indiscretions to which he had listened, he well knew how that vast property had been put together: it had been an epopee of cunning and perfidy, of ruthlessness and defiance of law, of luck too and of daring. Ferrara thought how interesting it would be to see a map in different colors showing successive acquisitions, as school textbooks do the expansion of the House of Savoy. Here at Gibilmonte was the embryo: six measures of wheat, half a hectare of vines, and a three-room hut, all that had been inherited by Don Batassano's father, Gaspare, an analphabetic of genius. In early youth he had seduced the deaf-and-dumb daughter of a smallholder scarcely less poor than himself, and with the dowry obtained by compulsory marriage doubled his holding. His wife, handicapped as she was, entered into her husband's game completely: by grinding thrift the couple accumulated a hoard which though tiny was precious in a place like Sicily, where hoarding at that period, as in the city-states of antiquity, was based exclusively on usury.

Shrewd loans had been granted, loans of a particular aspect which are made to people with property but insufficient income to pay interest. The lowing of Marta, Gaspare's wife, going around the village at dusk to exact her weekly dues, became proverbial. "When Marta's a-grunting, houses are tumbling." In ten years of gesticulating visits, in ten years of extorting crops from the Marchese Santapau whose sharecropper Gaspare was, in ten years of cautiously moved boundaries, in ten years of contented starvation, the couple's property had multiplied fivefold: he was only twenty-eight, the present Don Batassano seven. There had been a stormy period when the Bourbon legal authorities took it into their heads to inquire about one of the many corpses found out in the country: Gaspare had to keep away from Gibilmonte, and his wife gave out that he was staying with a cousin at Adernò to learn about mulberry growing; in reality every single night from nearby hills the doting Gaspare had watched smoke rising from the kitchen of his happy little home. Then came the Thousand, everything was upside down, inconvenient papers vanished from legal offices, and Gaspare Ibba returned home officially.

Everything was better than before. It was then that Gaspare thought up a move which seemed mad, like every stroke of genius; just as Napoleon at Austerlitz dared strip his center in order to trap the Austro-Russian boobies between his very strong flanks, so Gaspare mortgaged all his hard-fought land up to the hilt, and with the few thousand lire raised by this operation made a loan without interest to the Marchese Santapau, who was in difficulties due to donations to the Bourbon cause. The result was this: two years later the Santapau lost their estate of "Balate,"* which they had anyway never seen and from its name took to be sterile, all mortgages were off the Ibba property, Gaspare had become "Don Gaspare" and goat's meat was eaten at his home on Saturdays and Sundays. On reaching the goal of the first hundred thousand lire all went with the precision of a mechanical instrument: ecclesiastical properties were acquired for a tenth of their value by paying the first two installments of their wretched assessment; their buildings, the springs near by, the rights of way which they possessed, made it much easier to buy up surrounding lay properties that had lost value; the large incomes accruing went to the purchase or expropriation of other more distant lands.

So when Don Gaspare died still young his property

* Sicilian-Calabrian, from Arabic, meaning "paving slab."

was already of notable size; but like the Prussian territories in the middle of the eighteenth century, it consisted of large islands separated by the properties of others. To the son Batassano, as to King Frederick II, fell the task and the glory, first of unifying all in one single block, and then of moving the boundaries of the block itself toward more distant areas. Vineyards, olive and almond groves, pastures, ground rents, sowing land particularly, were annexed and digested, the incomes flowing into the shabby office at Gibilmonte where they stayed for a very short time and whence they soon issued, almost intact, to be transformed back into land. A wind of uninterrupted good fortune swelled the sails of the Ibba galleon: the name began to be pronounced with reverence throughout the whole poverty-stricken triangle of the island. Don Batassano meanwhile had married at the age of thirty, and not a handicapped creature like his venerated mother but a buxom girl of eighteen called Laura, daughter of the Gibilmonte notary; as dowry she brought her own health, a considerable sum in ready money, her father's valuable experience with the Curia, and a complete submission once her own considerable sexual needs were satisfied. Living proof of this submission of hers was eight children; a rough sunless happiness reigned in the Ibba household.

The accountant Ferrara was a person of sensitive feelings, a human species very rare in Sicily. His father had been an employee of the Salina administration in the stormy days of old Prince Fabrizio; and he himself, raised in the padded atmosphere of that household, had been accustomed to desiring a life commonplace indeed but calm; his own little sliver of princely cheese to nibble was enough for him. Those two big square meters of oiled paper evoked harsh and stubborn struggles within his soul, more rodent's than carnivore's. He had an impression of rereading the installments of La Cecilia's *History of the Bourbons of Naples* which his father, an advanced liberal, used to buy him every Saturday. Here at Gibilmonte, of course, were none of the imaginary orgies of Caserta described in that tract: here all was ruggedly, positively, puritanically evil. He took fright and left the room.

That evening at supper the whole family was present except for the eldest son, Gaspare, who was in Palermo with the excuse of preparing to retake his school-leaving

exams (he was already twenty). The meal was served
with rustic simplicity: all the cutlery, heavy and rich,
was heaped in the middle of the table and everyone
fished about in the pile according to his needs; the man-
servant Totò and the maidservant Mariannina were insistent on serving from the right. Signora Laura was the
picture of health in supreme flowering, that is, in major
rotundity; her well-shaped chin, her pretty nose, her eyes
expert in connubial delights, vanished into an exuberance
of still fresh, firm, and appetizing fat; the enormous bulk
of her body was covered in black silk, emblem of mourning perpetually renewed. Her sons Melchiorre, Pietro, and
Ignazio, her daughters Marta, Franceschina, Assunta,
and Paolina, showed alternating similarities, peculiar com-
binations of the rapacious features of their father and
the merciful ones of their mother. None, male or female,
had any taste whatsoever in dress: the girls were in
printed cretonnes (gray on white), the boys in sailor
suits, even the eldest among those present, Melchiorre,
whose budding seventeen-year-old mustache gave him an
odd air of some member of a royal suite. The conversation, or rather the dialogue, between Don Batassano and
Ferrara ranged exclusively around two subjects: the price

of land in the neighborhood of Palermo compared to that in the neighborhood of Gibilmonte, and gossip about aristocratic Palermo society. Don Batassano considered all those nobles as "starving," even those who had after all, if only in collections of antiques apart from incomes, fortunes equal to his own. Always shut away in his own parts, with rare trips to the local town and very rare journeys to Palermo in order to "follow" law cases in the courts, he did not know even one of these nobles personally, and had created an abstract and monotoned image of them, like that of the public for Harlequin or Captain Fracassa. Prince A. was a spendthrift, Prince B. a womanizer, Duke C. violent, Baron D. a gambler, Don Giuseppe E. a bully, Marchese F. "aesthetic" (he meant an "aesthete," a euphemism in its turn for something worse), and so on: each was a contemptible figure cut in cardboard. These opinions of Don Batassano's had a formidable propensity to error, and it might be said that there was no epithet which was not coupled erroneously to a name, and certainly no defect which was not fabulously exaggerated, the real defects of these persons meanwhile remaining unknown to him: obviously his mind worked in abstractions and took pleasure in contrasting the purity of the Ibbas with the corrupt background of the old nobility.

Ferrara knew rather more about these things, though with lacunae too, so that when he tried to contradict the more fantastic assertions he ran out of arguments; also his words aroused such moralistic indignation in Don Batassano that he soon fell silent; anyway they had now reached the end of the meal.

This, Ferrara considered, had been excellent; Donna Laura did not abandon herself to Pindaric flights in matters of food: she had Sicilian dishes served, numerous and highly flavored as possible, and thus murderous. Macaroni literally swam in oil of its own sauce and was buried under avalanches of *caciocavallo* cheese, meat was stuffed with incendiary salami, *zuppa in fretta* contained triple the cochineal, sugar, and candied fruit prescribed; but to Ferrara all that, as has been said, seemed exquisite and the apex of a really good table; at his rare luncheons in the Salina household he had always been disappointed by the insipidity of the food. Next day, though, on returning to Palermo, after handing over to Prince Fabrizietto the 78,200 lire, he described the meal offered him, and as he knew the Prince's predilection for *coulis de volaille* at the

Pré-Catalan and *timbales d'écrevisses* at Prunier's, he made sound horrible what he had in fact thought excellent; and thus he gave much pleasure to Salina who, during his "little game of poker" at the club later on, described every detail to his friends, who were ever avid for news of the legendary Ibbas; and all laughed till the moment when Peppino San Carlo announced impassively that he had a full house of queens.

As has been said, there was an acute curiosity about the Ibba family in the noble circles of Palermo. Curiosity is, after all, the mother of fables, and from it during those years were born hundreds of fantasies about that sudden fortune. These bore witness not only to the frothy and infantile imaginations of the upper classes, but also to an unconscious unease at seeing that, at the beginning of the twentieth century, a great fortune could be built up exclusively in land, this being a form of riches which, in the bitter experience of each of those gentlemen, was material for demolition unsuited to the construction of rich buildings. Those same landed proprietors felt that this modern reincarnation, in the Ibbas, of the vast grain-bearing possessions of the Chiaramonte and the Ventimiglia families of past centuries was irrational and dangerous for themselves, so they were all secretly against it; and that not only because this imposing edifice was erected largely from material which had once belonged to themselves, but because they took it as a sign of the permanent anachronism which is the brake on the wheels of the Sicilian cart, an anachronism realized by many but which no one, in fact, can evade or avoid collaborating with.

It should be repeated that this unease remained latent in their collective unconscious: it flowered only in the guise of jests and funny stories, as might be expected of a class with a low consumption of general ideas. A first and most elementary form of these was an exaggeration in figures, which with us are always elastic. Baldassare Ibba's fortune, though easy to check, was valued at dozens of million lire; one bold spirit even dared once to speak of "nearly a billion," but the effect was as if he had remained silent, for this sum, today so banal, was in such rare use in 1901 that nearly everyone was ignorant of its true meaning, and in those days of gold lire the phrase "a billion lire" really meant nothing at all. Analogous fantasies were woven about the origins of this fortune:

the humbleness of Don Batassano's origins were difficult
to exaggerate (old Corrado Finale, whose mother was a
Santapau, had hinted without saying so openly that Don
Batassano was the son of a brother-in-law of his who had
been in residence for some time at Gibilmonte, but the
story found little credit because Finale was known to
have a habit of attributing to himself or to his relatives
the clandestine parentage of any celebrity mentioned,
whether a victorious general or an acclaimed prima
donna); that modest corpse, though, which had been
such a brother to Don Gaspare, was multiplied tenfold,
a hundredfold, and every "elimination" that had taken
place in Sicily over the last thirty years (and there had
been quite a number) was put down to the Ibbas, who
were, after all, legally unimpeachable. This, surprising
though it may seem, was the legend's most benevolent
part, because deeds of violence, when unpunished, were
at that time a motive for esteem, the halo of Sicilian
saints being blood-red.

To these inventions grown from seed were added others
grafted: for instance out came, refurbished, a tale told
a hundred years before about Testasecca, who caused a
little channel to be scooped, collected his hundreds of

cows and thousands of sheep on a hillock above, had them milked all at the same moment, and so presented King Ferdinand IV with the sight of a small stream of milk flowing warm and frothing at his feet. This fable, which is not without a certain pastoral poetry that should have suggested its origin in Theocritus, was now adapted to Don Batassano by the simple substitution of King Umberto I of Italy for King Ferdinand of the Two Sicilies; and though it was quite easy to prove that the former sovereign had never set foot on any Ibba land the fable persisted, unrefuted.

It was for these reasons of rancor mingled with fear that, when the "little game of poker" was over, conversation again fell on the subject of the Ibbas. The dozen members present had settled down on the terrace of the club, which overlooked a placid courtyard and was shaded by a tall tree raining petals of lilac down on those gentlemen, most of whom were old. Footmen in red and blue brought around ice and cool soft drinks. From the depths of a wicker armchair came the ever choleric tones of Santa Giulia. "Well, could someone please tell me how much land these blessed Ibbas really do own?"

"Someone could, and will. Fourteen thousand three

hundred and twenty-five hectares," replied San Carlo coldly.

"Is that all? I thought more."

"Fourteen thousand, balls! People who have been there say it can't be less than twenty thousand hectares, sure as death and taxes; and all first-class crop-bearing land."

General Làscari, who seemed immersed in reading *La Tribuna,* brusquely lowered the newspaper and showed his liverish visage embroidered with yellow lines in which very white eyeballs showed up hard and rather sinister, like the eyes of some Greek bronzes. "Twenty-eight thousand they are, neither more nor less; I was told by my nephew who is a cousin of the local prefect's wife. That's it, once and for all; there's no need to discuss it any longer."

Pippo Follonica, a visiting guest from Rome, burst out laughing. "But if you're all so interested, why not send someone down to the Land Registry? It's easy to know the truth, this truth anyway."

This rational suggestion got a cold reception. Follonica did not understand the passionate, nonstatistical nature of the discussion; these gentlemen were tossing about among themselves envies, rancors, and anxieties, all emotions which no Land Registry certificates could assuage.

The General grew furious. "When I tell you something there's no need for any registry whatsoever." Then politeness toward a guest softened him. "My dear Prince, you don't know what our Land Registry office is like! Transfers of property are never recorded and people still figure as owners who've sold up and are now in the poorhouse."

Faced with so detailed a denial, Follonica changed tactics. "Let's admit that the number of hectares remains unknown; even so the value of property in the hands of this boor who excites you all must be known!"

"Perfectly well known: eight million exactly."

"Balls!" That was the inevitable opening to any phrase from Santa Giulia. "Balls! Not a cent less than twelve!"

"What a world you live in! You don't know anything! There's twenty-five million in land alone. Then there are ground rents, capital on loan and not yet transformed into property, the value of cattle. Another five million at least." The General had put down his newspaper and was getting worked up. His peremptory manner had for years irritated the entire club, each member of which wished to be the only one making incontrovertible affirmations; so that a coalition of reawakened antipathies at once formed against his opinion, and without any reference to major or minor truths the estimate of the Ibba property slumped. "That's all poetic nonsense; money and sanctity, believe half of a half, as the proverb goes. If Batassano Ibba has ten million all told that's more than enough." The figure had been distilled from nothing at all, that is from polemical necessity; but when said, as it responded to everyone's wishes it calmed all except the General, who went on gesticulating from deep in his armchair, impotent against his nine adversaries.

A footman entered carrying a long wooden pole at the end of which was a wick dipped in spirit. The gentle light of dusk changed to the harsh glare of a gas chandelier. The guest from Rome was much amused: it was his first visit to Sicily, and during the five days of his stay in Palermo he had been invited to a number of houses and had begun to change his opinions about what he had presumed to be the provincialism of Palermo; dinners had been well served, drawing rooms splendid, ladies graceful. But now this impassioned discussion about the fortune of an individual whom none of the contestants knew nor wanted to know, these patent exaggerations, this convulsive gesticulating about nothing, made him reverse, reminded him a little too closely of conversations heard at Fondi or Palestrina when he had to go out there to see about his estates, or maybe even at the druggist Bésuquet's, of which he had preserved a happy memory since his reading of *Tartarin;** and he began laying in a store of tales to regale friends on his return to Rome a week later. But he was wrong: too much a man of fashion ever to probe much deeper than the obvious, what appeared to him as a humorous exhibition of provincialism was anything but comic: this was the tragic jerking of a class which was seeing the end of its own landowning supremacy, that is, of its own reason for existence and its own social continuity, and which in these willful exaggerations and artificial diminutions sought outlets for its anger, relief for its fear.

The truth being impossible to establish, the conversation deviated: it was still investigating Batassano Ibba's private affairs but now turned to consider his personal life.

"He lives like a monk; gets up at four in the morning; goes out into the marketplace to engage day laborers,

* *Tartarin de Tarascon*, by Alphonse Daudet.

is busy with estate management the whole day long, eats only pasta and vegetables in oil, and is in bed by eight."

Salina protested, "A monk with a wife and eight children, let's remember. An employee of mine spent forty-eight hours at his house: it's ugly but it's big and comfortable, decent in fact; the wife seems to have been pretty, the children well dressed; in fact one of them is here in Palermo to study; and the food at his table is heavy but plentiful, as I've already told you."

The General stuck to his guns: "You, Salina, believe everything you're told; or rather, they wanted to throw dust in the eyes of your man, who must be an idiot. Bread, cheese, and oil lamps, that's Ibba's daily routine, his real life; when someone comes from Palermo he obviously tries to put up a show, to dazzle us, so he deludes himself."

Santa Giulia, under the impetus of the news he wanted to communicate, was jumping about in his armchair; his well-shod feet banged the floor, his hands trembled, and the ash of his cigarette snowed all over his suit. "Balls, gentlemen! Gentlemen, balls! You're utterly mistaken. I'm the only one who really knows about this: the wife of one of my keepers comes from Torrebella, a few steps from Gibilmonte; every now and again she goes to see

her sister who is married there and has told her everything. One can't be more certain than that, I think." He
sought for a confirmation of his own certainty in everyone's eyes and, as all were amused, easily found it. Although there was no bashful ear to be respected he lowered
his voice: without this melodramatic preamble the effect
of his revelations would never have been the same.

"Four kilometers from Gibilmonte, Don Batassano
has had a small house built; the most luxurious place
imaginable, furnished by Salci and all that." Reminis-
cences of reading Catulle Mendès, nostalgic memories of
Parisian brothels, unrealized though long-nursed yearn-
ings, stirred his imagination. "He had Rochegrosse come
from Paris to fresco all the rooms: the great painter was
three months at Gibilmonte and demanded a hundred
thousand lire a month." (Rochegrosse had in fact been in
Sicily two years before: he had remained a week with
his wife and three children, and left again after quietly
visiting the Capella Palatina, Segesta, and the Latomie
of Syracuse.) "It cost a fortune! But what frescoes he
did! Enough to bring a dead man to life! Naked women,
quite naked, dancing, drinking, and coupling with men
and with each other in every position, in every conceivable

manner. Masterpieces! An encyclopedia, I tell you, an encyclopedia of pleasures! Just let a Parisian loose with a hundred thousand lire a month! There Ibba receives women by the dozen: Italian, French, German, Spanish. La Otero was there too, I know that for a fact. That Batassano has made his *Parc aux Cerfs* there, like Louis the Fifteenth."

This time Santa Giulia really had caused a sensation: everyone sat listening to him open-mouthed. Not that he was believed, but they found this fantasy a highly poetic one and each longed to have Ibba's millions so that others could invent similar splendid nonsense about himself. The first to shake off the spell was the General: "And how d'you come to know that? Have you been into the house yourself, pray? As odalisque or eunuch?" They laughed, Santa Guilia laughed too. "I told you: the wife of my keeper Antonio has seen those paintings."

"Fine! Then you've a keeper who's a cuckold."

"Cuckold, balls! She went there to take some sheets which she'd washed. They didn't let her in, but a window was open and she saw it all."

The castle of lies was obviously of extreme fragility; but it was of such beauty, with its female thighs and nameless obscenities, its famous painters and hundred-thousand-lire notes, that no one had any desire to give it a puff and bring it down.

Salina pulled out his watch: *"Mamma mia!* Eight o'clock already! I must go home and dress: there's *Traviata* tonight at the Politeama, and that 'Amami, Alfredo' of La Bellincioni's is not to be missed. See you in the club boxes!"